THE EQUINOX OF THE GODS

A.·.A.·. Publication in Class E.

93	10° = 1□	Pro Coll. Summ.
666	9° = 2□	
777	8° = 3□	

V. N.	Præmonstrator	Pro Coll. Ext.
P.	Imperator	
Achad.	Cancellarius	

I. W. E.	7° = 4□	Pro Coll. Int.
O. M.	7° = 4□	
O. S. V.	6° = 5□	
Parsival.	5° = 6□	

THE EQUINOX OF THE GODS

The Official Organ of the A.·.A.·.

Do what thou wilt shall be the whole of the Law.
Love is the law, love under will.
The word of the law is
θελημα
The Official Organ of the O.T.O.

Deus  Homo

est

Vol. III. No. III

An IIIxxi ☉ in ♎

SEPTEMBER MCMXCI E. V.

Issued by the O.T.O.
in association with
NEW FALCON PUBLICATIONS

New Falcon Publications
7025 First Avenue, #5
Scottsdale, AZ 85251 USA.

A limited leather-bound edition is available
from New Falcon Publications.

Also published in cloth as *The Equinox* III(3) by
93 Publishing Ltd., JAF Box 7865, New York, NY 10116-4634

First edition published in 1936 EV by Ordo Templi Orientis, London.
This corrected facsimile edition issued in 1991 EV
by Ordo Templi Orientis, International Headquarters,
JAF Box 7666, New York, NY 10116 USA.

ISBN 1-56184-028-9

Printed in the United States of America.

The paper used in this publication meets the minimum requirements
of the American National Standard for Permanence of Paper for
Printed Library Materials Z39.48-1984

NOTE TO THE FACSIMILE EDITION

Do what thou wilt shall be the whole of the Law.

THE FIRST EDITION of *The Equinox of the Gods*, privately published in London by the O.T.O. in 1936 EV, was limited to 1000 copies, with an additional 250 subscriber's copies. Although a second printing was issued the following year, the work remains one of Crowley's rarest magical books. This is only partly due to the relatively small number of copies produced, and the constant demand among students of Crowley's work. It is also attributable to the physical beauty of the first edition, printed in a large Crown Quarto format (8½" × 11") in a generous 15 point Bembo. The MS of *The Book of the Law* was printed, one side only, as 65 separate 8" × 10" sheets. These were placed loose in a handmade paper folder fitted into a pocket in the inside back cover. The title page for *Liber XXXI* and the Comment were printed on the folder in red and black ink.

This facsimile edition differs from the first edition in several respects. The text has been reduced photographically by 10% to accommodate a 6" × 9" page size with no significant sacrifice of readability. This edition corrects seventeen typographical errors listed in the errata slip issued with the 1937 EV second printing of the first edition; a few additional textual corrections have been made as well. The color reproduction of the Stèle of Revealing in the first edition is of poor quality; for this edition the Stèle published in *The Equinox* I(7) in 1912 EV is used. Also, the order of the obverse and reverse sides of the Stèle have been changed; they appeared in reverse order in the first edition. The MS of *The Book of the Law* is bound into the text, as are the title page for *Liber XXXI* and the Comment. Finally, the appropriate changes have been made to the Table of Contents to reflect these variations.

Love is the law, love under will.

HYMENAEUS BETA
Frater Superior, O.T.O.

CONTENTS

ILLUSTRATIONS

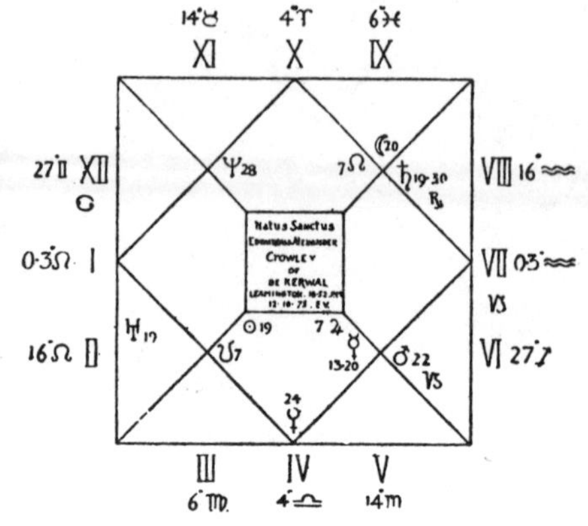

THE NATIVITY OF FRA. P.

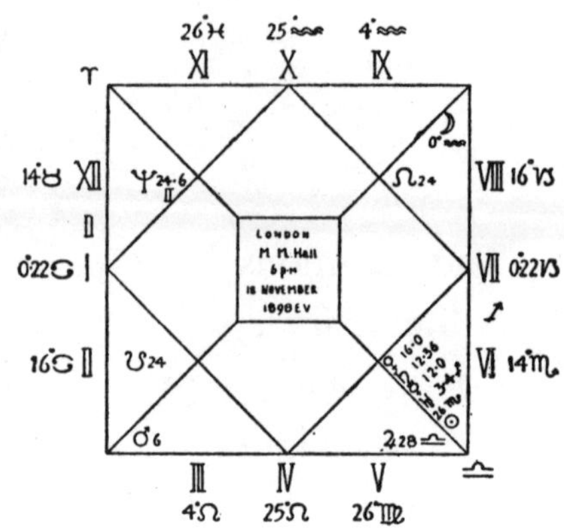

THE FIRST INITIATION OF FRA. P.

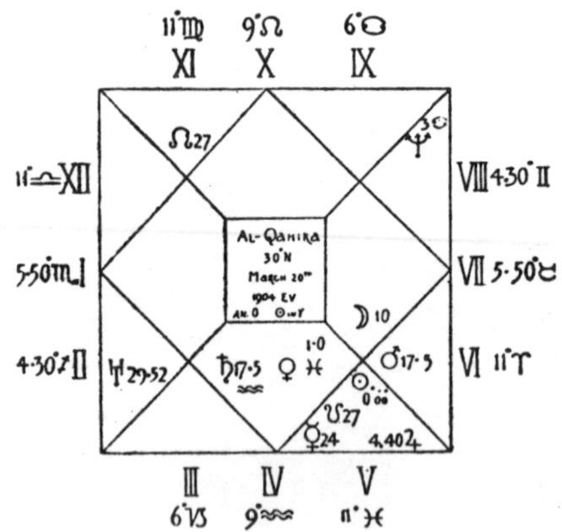

THE EQUINOX OF THE GODS

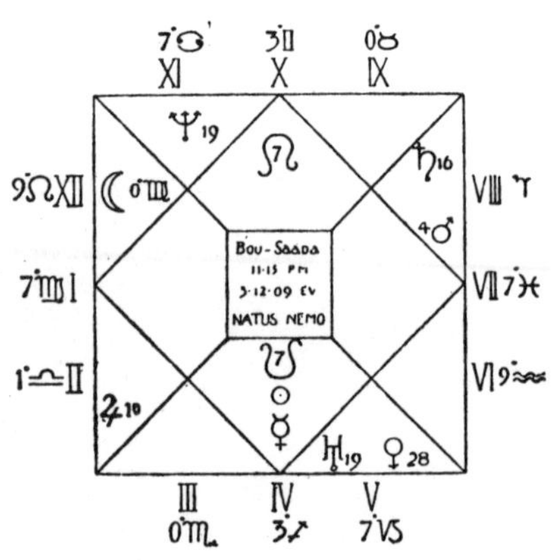

THE ANNIHILATION OF FRA. P.

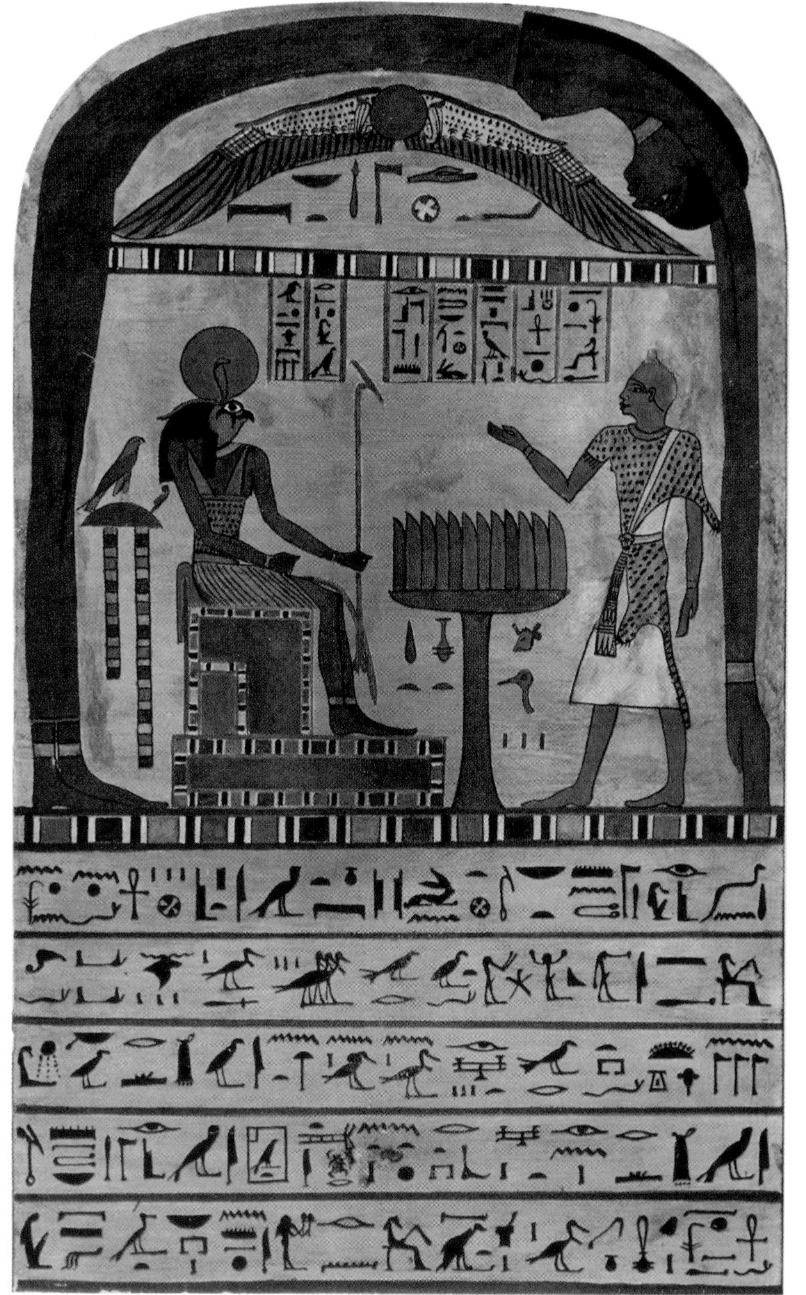

A PARAPHRASE OF THE INSCRIPTIONS UPON THE OBVERSE OF THE STÉLÉ OF REVEALING

Above, the gemmèd azure is
  The naked splendour of Nuit;
She bends in ecstasy to kiss
  The secret ardours of Hadit.
The wingèd globe, the starry blue
Are mine, o Ankh-f-n-Khonsu.

I am the Lord of Thebes, and I
  The inspired forth-speaker of Mentu;
For me unveils the veilèd sky,
  The self-slain Ankh-f-n-Khonsu
Whose words are truth. I invoke, I greet
Thy presence, o Ra-Hoor-Khuit!

Unity uttermost showed!
  I adore the might of Thy breath,
Supreme and terrible God,
  Who makest the gods and death
    To tremble before Thee:—
    I, I adore thee!

Appear on the throne of Ra!
  Open the ways of the Khu!
Lighten the ways of the Ka!
  The ways of the Khabs run through
    To stir me or still me!
    Aum! let it kill me!

The Light is mine; its rays consume
  Me: I have made a secret door
Into the House of Ra and Tum,
  Of Khephra, and of Ahathoor.
I am thy Theban, o Mentu,
The prophet Ankh-f-n-Khonsu!

By Bes-na-Maut my breast I beat;
  By wise Ta-Nech I weave my spell.
Show thy star-splendour, O Nuith!
  Bid me within thine House to dwell,
O wingèd snake of light, Hadith!
Abide with me, Ra-Hoor-Khuit!

A PARAPHRASE OF THE HIEROGLYPHS OF THE 11 LINES UPON THE REVERSE OF THE STÉLÉ

Saith of Mentu the truth-telling brother
  Who was master of Thebes from his birth:
O heart of me, heart of my mother!
  O heart which I had upon earth!
Stand not thou up against me a witness!
  Oppose me not, judge, in my quest!
Accuse me not now of unfitness
  Before the Great God, the dread Lord of the West!
For I fastened the one to the other
  With a spell for their mystical girth,
The earth and the wonderful West,
  When I flourished, o earth, on thy breast!

The dead man Ankh-f-n-Khonsu
  Saith with his voice of truth and calm:
O thou that hast a single arm!
  O thou that glitterest in the moon!
I weave thee in the spinning charm;
  I lure thee with the billowy tune.

The dead man Ankh-f-n-Khonsu
  Hath parted from the darkling crowds,
Hath joined the dwellers of the light,
  Opening Duant, the star-abodes,
  Their keys receiving.
The dead man Ankh-f-n-Khonsu
  Hath made his passage into night,
His pleasure on the earth to do
  Among the living.

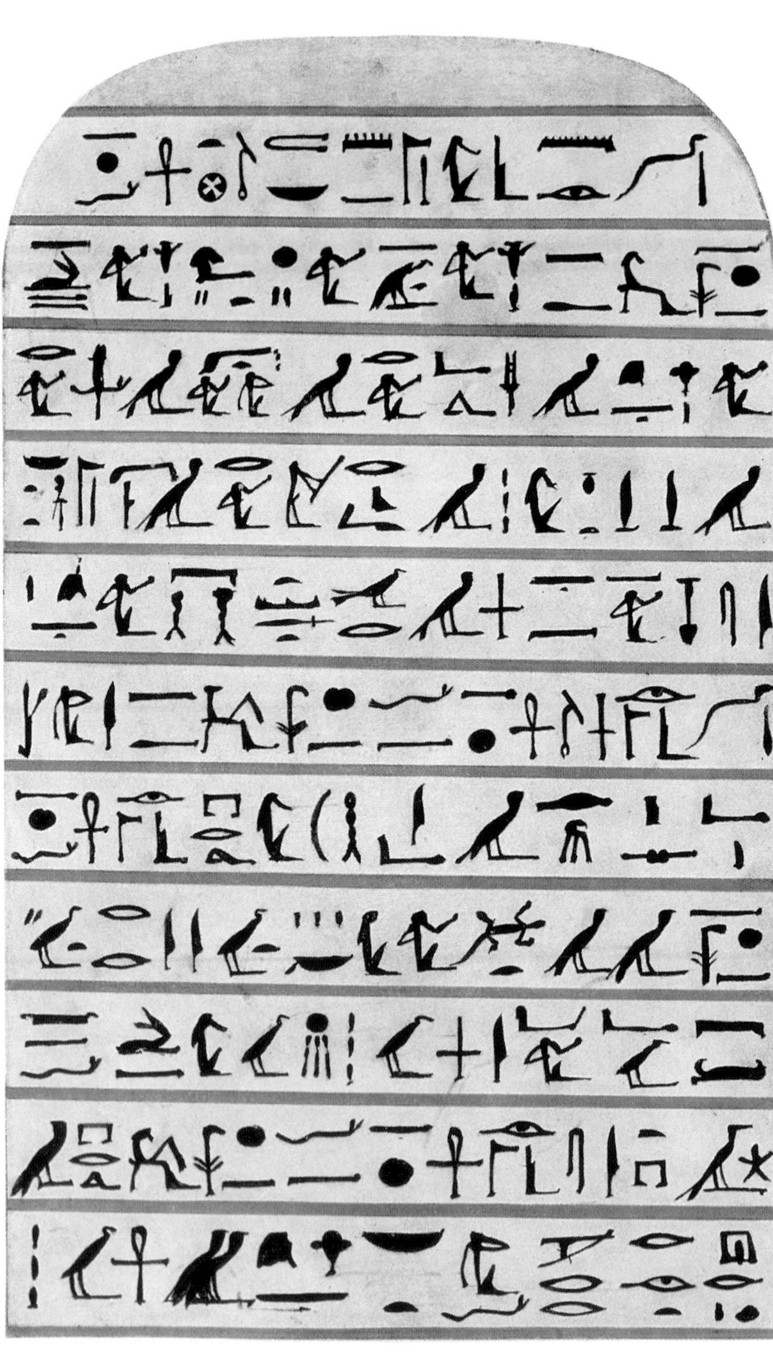

THE SUMMONS.

On April 8, 9 and 10, 1904, e.v. this book was dictated to 666 (Aleister Crowley) by Aiwass, a Being whose nature he does not fully understand, but who described Himself as "the Minister of Hoor-Paar-Kraat" (the Lord of Silence).

The contents of the book prove to strict scientific demonstration that He possesses knowledge and power quite beyond anything that has been hitherto associated with human faculties.

The circumstances of the dictation are described in the *Equinox,* Vol. I, No. vii: but a fuller account, with an outline of the proof of the character of the book, is now here to be issued.

The book announces a New Law for mankind.

It replaces the moral and religious sanctions of the past, which have everywhere broken down, by a principle valid for each man and woman in the world, and self-evidently indefeasible.

The spiritual Revolution announced by the book has already taken place: hardly a country where it is not openly manifest.

Ignorance of the true meaning of this new Law has led to gross anarchy. Its conscious adoption in its proper sense is the sole cure for the political, social and racial unrest which have brought about the World War, the catastrophe of Europe and America, and the threatening attitude of China, India and Islam.

Its solution of the fundamental problems of mathematics and philosophy will establish a new epoch in history.

But it must not be supposed that so potent an instrument of energy can be used without danger.

I summon, therefore, by the power and authority entrusted to me, every great spirit and mind now on this planet incarnate to take effective hold of this transcendent force, and apply it to the advancement of the welfare of the human race.

For as the experience of these two and thirty years has shown too terribly, the book cannot be ignored. It has leavened Mankind unaware: and Man must make thereof the Bread of Life. Its ferment has begun to work on the grape of thought: Man must obtain therefrom the Wine of Ecstasy.

Come then, all ye, in the Name of the Lord of the Aeon, the Crowned and Conquering Child, Heru-Ra-Ha: I call ye to partake this sacrament.

Know—will—dare—and be silent!

The Priest of the Princes,

ANKH-AF-NA-KHONSU.

A SUMMARY

MARSYAS. (As for The Beast 666).
I bear a message. Heaven hath sent
The knowledge of a new sweet way
Into the Secret Element.

OLYMPAS. (Any Aspirant)
Master, while yet the glory clings
Declare this mystery magical!

MARSYAS.
I am yet borne on these blue wings
Into the Essence of the All.
Now, now I stand on earth again,
Though, blazing through each nerve and vein,
The light yet holds its choral course,
Filling my frame with fiery force
Like God's. Now hear the Apocalypse
New-fledged on these reluctant lips!

OLYMPAS.
I tremble like an aspen, quiver
Like light upon a rainy river!

MARSYAS.
Do what thou wilt! is the sole word
Of law that my attainment heard.
Arise, and lay thine hand on God!
Arise, and set a period
Unto Restriction! That is sin:

To hold thine holy spirit in !
O thou that chafest at thy bars,
Invoke Nuit beneath her stars
With a pure heart (Her incense burned
Of gums and woods, in gold inurned)
And let the serpent flame therein
A little, and thy soul shall win
To lie within her bosom. Lo !
Thou wouldst give all——and she cries : No !
Take all, and take me ! Gather spice
And virgins and great pearls of price !
Worship me in a single robe,
Crowned Richly ! Girdle of the globe,
I love thee. Pale and purple, veiled,
Voluptuous, swan silver-sailed,
I love thee. I am drunkenness
Of the inmost sense, my soul's caress
Is toward thee ! Let my priestess stand
Bare and rejoicing, softly fanned
By smooth-lipped acolytes, upon
Mine iridescent altar-stone,
And in her love-chaunt swooningly
Say evermore : To me ! To me !
I am the azure-lidded daughter
Of sunset ; the all-girdling water ;
The naked brilliance of the sky
In the voluptuous night am I !
With song, with jewel, with perfume,
Wake all my rose's blush and bloom !
Drink to me ! Love me ! I love thee,
My love, my lord—to me ! to me !

OLYMPAS. There is no harshness in the breath
Of this—is life surpassed, and death?

MARSYAS. There is the Snake that gives delight
And Knowledge, stirs the heart aright
With drunkenness. Strange drugs are thine,
Hadit, and draughts of wizard wine!
These do no hurt. Thine hermits dwell
Not in the cold secretive cell,
But under purple canopies
With mighty-breasted mistresses
Magnificent as lionesses—
Tender and terrible caresses!
Fire lives, and light, in eager eyes;
And massed huge hair about them lies.
They lead their hosts to victory:
In every joy they are kings; then see
That secret serpent coiled to spring
And win the world! O priest and king,
Let there be feasting, foining, fighting,
A revel of lusting, singing, smiting!
Work; be the bed of work! Hold! Hold!
The stars' kiss is as molten gold.
Harden! Hold thyself up! now die—
Ah! Ah! Exceed! Exceed!

OLYMPAS. And I?

MARSYAS. My stature shall surpass the stars:
He hath said it! Men shall worship me
In hidden woods, on barren scaurs,
Henceforth to all eternity.

OLYMPAS. Hail! I adore thee! Let us feast.

MARSYAS. I am the consecrated Beast.
I build the Abominable House.
The Scarlet Woman is my Spouse—

OLYMPAS. What is this word?

MARSYAS. Thou canst not know
Till thou hast passed the Fourth Ordeal.

OLYMPAS. I worship thee. The moon-rays flow
Masterfully rich and real
From thy red mouth, and burst, young suns
Chanting before the Holy Ones
Thine Eight Mysterious Orisons!

MARSYAS. The last spell! The availing word!
The two completed by the third!
The Lord of War, of Vengeance
That slayeth with a single glance!
This light is in me of my Lord.
His Name is this far-whirling sword.
I push His order. Keen and swift
My Hawk's eye flames; these arms uplift
The Banner of Silence and of Strength—
Hail! Hail! thou art here, my Lord, at length!
Lo, the Hawk-Headed Lord am I:
My nemyss shrouds the night-blue sky.
Hail! ye twin warriors that guard

The pillars of the world! Your time
Is nigh at hand. The snake that marred
Heaven with his inexhaustible slime
Is slain; I bear the Wand of power,
The Wand that waxes and that wanes;
I crush the Universe this hour
In my left hand; and naught remains!
Ho! for the splendour in my name
Hidden and glorious, a flame
Secretly shooting from the sun.
Aum! Ha!—my destiny is done.
The Word is spoken and concealed.

OLYMPAS. I am stunned. What wonder was revealed?

MARSYAS. The rite is secret.

OLYMPAS. Profits it?

MARSYAS. Only to wisdom and to wit.

OLYMPAS. The other did no less.

MARSYAS. Then prove
Both by the master-key of Love.
The lock turns stiffly? Shalt thou shirk
To use the sacred oil of work?
Not from the valley shalt thou wrest
The eggs that line the eagle's nest!
Climb, with thy life at stake, the ice,

The sheer wall of the precipice!
Master the cornice, gain the breach,
And learn what next the ridge can teach!
Yet—not the ridge itself may speak
The secret of the final peak.

OLYMPAS. All ridges join at last.

MARSYAS. Admitted,
O thou astute and subtle-witted!
Yet one—loose, jagged, clad in mist!
Another—firm, smooth, loved and kissed
By the soft sun! Our order hath
This secret of the solar path,
Even as our Lord the Beast hath won
The mystic Number of the Sun.

OLYMPAS. These secrets are too high for me.

MARSYAS. Nay, little brother! Come and see!
Neither by faith nor fear nor awe
Approach the doctrine of the Law!
Truth, Courage, Love, shall win the bout,
And those three others be cast out.

OLYMPAS. Lead me, Master, by the hand
Gently to this gracious land!
Let me drink the doctrine in,
An all-healing medicine!
Let me rise, correct and firm,

Steady striding to the term,
Master of my fate, to rise
To imperial destinies;
With the sun's ensanguine dart
Spear-bright in my blazing heart,
And my being's basil-plant
Bright and hard as adamant!

MARSYAS. Yonder, faintly luminous,
The yellow desert waits for us.
Lithe and eager, hand in hand,
We travel to the lonely land.
There, beneath the stars, the smoke
Of our incense shall invoke
The Queen of Space; and subtly She
Shall bend from Her Infinity
Like a lambent flame of blue,
Touching us, and piercing through
All the sense-webs that we are
As the aethyr penetrates a star!
Her hands caressing the black earth,
Her sweet lithe body arched for love,
Her feet a Zephyr to the flowers,
She calls my name—she gives the sign
That she is mine, supremely mine,
And clinging to the infinite girth
My soul gets perfect joy thereof
Beyond the abysses and the hours;
So that—I kiss her lovely brows;
She bathes my body in perfume

Of sweat . . . . O thou my secret spouse,
Continuous One of Heaven! illume
My soul with this arcane delight,
Voluptuous Daughter of the Night!
Eat me up wholly with the glance
Of thy luxurious brilliance!

OLYMPAS. The desert calls.

MARSYAS. Then let us go!
Or seek the sacramental snow,
Where like an high-priest I may stand
With acolytes on every hand,
The lesser peaks—my will withdrawn
To invoke the dayspring from the dawn,
Changing that rosy smoke of light
To a pure crystalline white;
Though the mist of mind, as draws
A dancer round her limbs the gauze,
Clothe Light, and show the virgin Sun
A lemon-pale medallion!
Thence leap we leashless to the goal,
Stainless star-rapture of the soul.
So the altar-fires fade
As the Godhead is displayed.
Nay, we stir not. Everywhere
Is our temple right appointed.
All the earth is faery fair
For us. Am I not anointed?
The Sigil burns upon the brow
At the adjuration—here and now.

OLYMPAS. The air is laden with perfumes.

MARSYAS. Behold! it beams—it burns—it blooms.

. . . . . .

OLYMPAS. Master, how subtly hast thou drawn
The daylight from the Golden Dawn,
Bidden the Cavernous Mount unfold
Its Ruby Rose, its Cross of Gold;
Until I saw, flashed from afar,
The Hawk's Eye in the Silver Star!

MARSYAS. Peace to all beings. Peace to thee,
Co-heir of mine eternity!
Peace to the greatest and the least,
To nebula and nenuphar!
Light in abundance be increased
On them that dream that shadows are!

OLYMPAS. Blessing and worship to The Beast,
The prophet of the lovely Star!

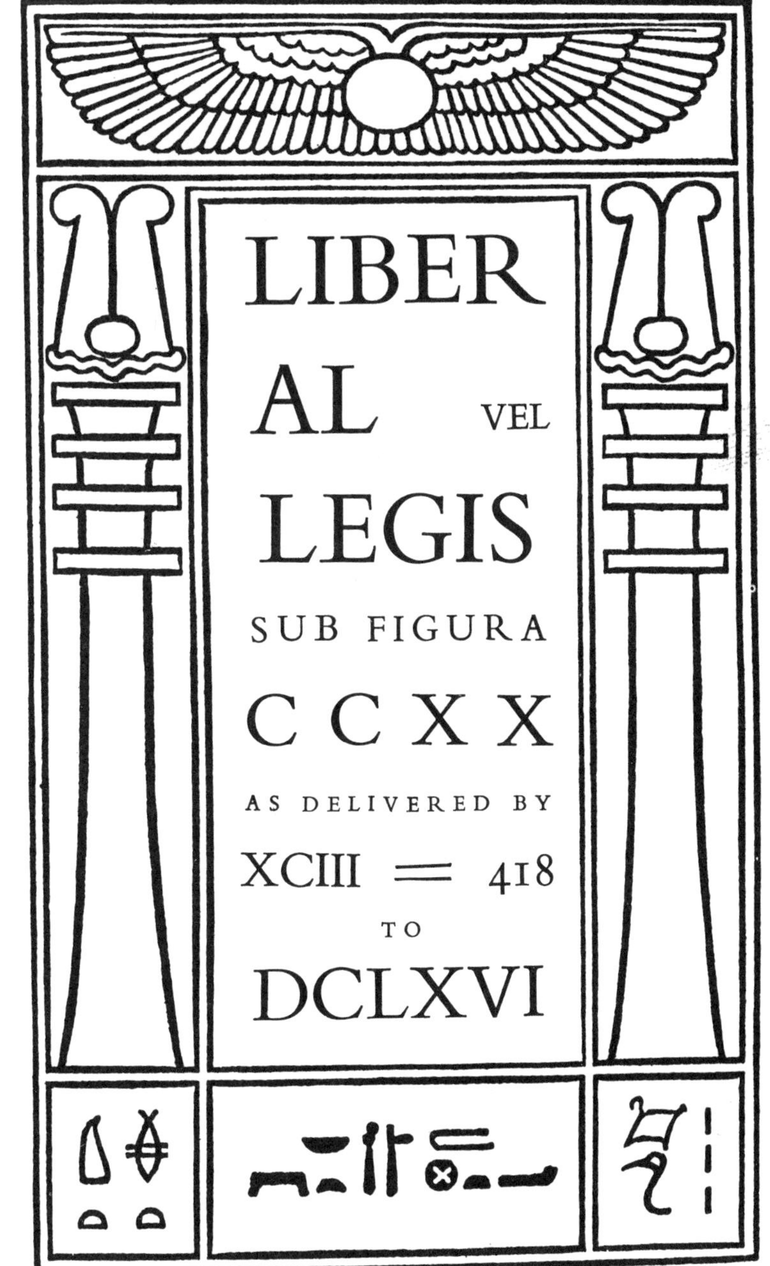
LIBER
AL VEL
LEGIS
SUB FIGURA
CCXX
AS DELIVERED BY
XCIII = 418
TO
DCLXVI

A∴A∴ Publication in Class A.

93	$10^\circ = 1^\square$	Pro Coll. Summ.
666	$9^\circ = 2^\square$	
777	$8^\circ = 3^\square$	

V. N.	Præmonstrator	Pro Coll. Ext.
P.	Imperator	
Achad.	Cancellarius	

I. W. E.	$7^\circ = 4^\square$	Pro Coll. Int.
O. M.	$7^\circ = 4^\square$	
O. S. V.	$6^\circ = 5^\square$	
Parsival.	$5^\circ = 6^\square$	

1. Had! The manifestation of Nuit.

2. The unveiling of the company of heaven.

3. Every man and every woman is a star.

4. Every number is infinite; there is no difference.

5. Help me, o warrior lord of Thebes, in my unveiling before the Children of men!

6. Be thou Hadit, my secret centre, my heart & my tongue!

7. Behold! it is revealed by Aiwass the minister of Hoor-paar-kraat.

8. The Khabs is in the Khu, not the Khu in the Khabs.

9. Worship then the Khabs, and behold my light shed over you!

10. Let my servants be few & secret: they shall rule the many & the known.

11. These are fools that men adore; both their Gods & their men are fools.

12. Come forth, o children, under the stars, & take your fill of love!

13. I am above you and in you. My ecstasy is in yours. My joy is to see your joy.

14. Above, the gemmèd azure is
    The naked splendour of Nuit;
  She bends in ecstasy to kiss
    The secret ardours of Hadit.

The wingèd globe, the starry blue,
Are mine, O Ankh-af-na-khonsu!

15. Now ye shall know that the chosen priest & apostle of infinite space is the prince-priest the Beast; and in his woman called the Scarlet Woman is all power given. They shall gather my children into their fold: they shall bring the glory of the stars into the hearts of men.

16. For he is ever a sun, and she a moon. But to him is the winged secret flame, and to her the stooping starlight.

17. But ye are not so chosen.

18. Burn upon their brows, o splendrous serpent!

19. O azure-lidded woman, bend upon them!

20. The key of the rituals is in the secret word which I have given unto him.

21. With the God & the Adorer I am nothing: they do not see me. They are as upon the earth; I am Heaven, and there is no other God than me, and my lord Hadit.

22. Now, therefore, I am known to ye by my name Nuit, and to him by a secret name which I will give him when at last he knoweth me. Since I am Infinite Space, and the Infinite Stars thereof, do ye also thus. Bind nothing! Let there be no difference made among you between any one thing & any other thing; for thereby there cometh hurt.

23. But whoso availeth in this, let him be the chief of all!

24. I am Nuit, and my word is six and fifty.

25. Divide, add, multiply, and understand.

26. Then saith the prophet and slave of the beauteous one: Who am I, and what shall be the sign? So she answered him, bending down, a lambent flame of blue, all-touching, all penetrant, her lovely hands upon the black earth, & her lithe

body arched for love, and her soft feet not hurting the little flowers: Thou knowest! And the sign shall be my ecstasy, the consciousness of the continuity of existence, the omnipresence of my body.

27. Then the priest answered & said unto the Queen of Space, kissing her lovely brows, and the dew of her light bathing his whole body in a sweet-smelling perfume of sweat: O Nuit, continuous one of Heaven, let it be ever thus; that men speak not of Thee as One but as None; and let them speak not of thee at all, since thou art continuous!

28. None, breathed the light, faint & faery, of the stars, and two.

29. For I am divided for love's sake, for the chance of union.

30. This is the creation of the world, that the pain of division is as nothing, and the joy of dissolution all.

31. For these fools of men and their woes care not thou at all! They feel little; what is, is balanced by weak joys; but ye are my chosen ones.

32. Obey my prophet! follow out the ordeals of my knowledge! seek me only! Then the joys of my love will redeem ye from all pain. This is so: I swear it by the vault of my body; by my sacred heart and tongue; by all I can give, by all I desire of ye all.

33. Then the priest fell into a deep trance or swoon, & said unto the Queen of Heaven; Write unto us the ordeals; write unto us the rituals; write unto us the law!

34. But she said: the ordeals I write not: the rituals shall be half known and half concealed: the Law is for all.

35. This that thou writest is the threefold book of Law.

36. My scribe Ankh-af-na-khonsu, the priest of the princes,

shall not in one letter change this book; but lest there be folly, he shall comment thereupon by the wisdom of Ra-Hoor-Khu-it.

37. Also the mantras and spells; the obeah and the wanga; the work of the wand and the work of the sword; these he shall learn and teach.

38. He must teach; but he may make severe the ordeals.

39. The word of the Law is θελημα.

40. Who calls us Thelemites will do no wrong, if he look but close into the word. For there are therein Three Grades, the Hermit, and the Lover, and the man of Earth. Do what thou wilt shall be the whole of the Law.

41. The word of Sin is Restriction. O man! refuse not thy wife, if she will! O lover, if thou wilt, depart! There is no bond that can unite the divided but love: all else is a curse. Accurséd! Accurséd be it to the aeons! Hell.

42. Let it be that state of manyhood bound and loathing. So with thy all; thou hast no right but to do thy will.

43. Do that, and no other shall say nay.

44. For pure will, unassuaged of purpose, delivered from the lust of result, is every way perfect.

45. The Perfect and the Perfect are one Perfect and not two; nay, are none!

46. Nothing is a secret key of this law. Sixty-one the Jews call it; I call it eight, eighty, four hundred & eighteen.

47. But they have the half: unite by thine art so that all disappear.

48. My prophet is a fool with his one, one, one; are not they the Ox, and none by the Book?

49. Abrogate are all rituals, all ordeals, all words and

signs. Ra-Hoor-Khuit hath taken his seat in the East at the Equinox of the Gods; and let Asar be with Isa, who also are one. But they are not of me. Let Asar be the adorant, Isa the sufferer; Hoor in his secret name and splendour is the Lord initiating.

50. There is a word to say about the Hierophantic task. Behold! there are three ordeals in one, and it may be given in three ways. The gross must pass through fire; let the fine be tried in intellect, and the lofty chosen ones in the highest. Thus ye have star & star, system & system; let not one know well the other!

51. There are four gates to one palace; the floor of that palace is of silver and gold; lapis lazuli & jasper are there; and all rare scents; jasmine & rose, and the emblems of death. Let him enter in turn or at once the four gates; let him stand on the floor of the palace. Will he not sink? Amn. Ho! warrior, if thy servant sink? But there are means and means. Be goodly therefore: dress ye all in fine apparel; eat rich foods and drink sweet wines and wines that foam! Also, take your fill and will of love as ye will, when, where and with whom ye will! But always unto me.

52. If this be not aright; if ye confound the space-marks, saying: They are one; or saying, They are many; if the ritual be not ever unto me: then expect the direful judgments of Ra Hoor Khuit!

53. This shall regenerate the world, the little world my sister, my heart & my tongue, unto whom I send this kiss. Also, o scribe and prophet, though thou be of the princes, it shall not assuage thee nor absolve thee. But ecstasy be thine and joy of earth: ever To me! To me!

54. Change not as much as the style of a letter; for behold! thou, o prophet, shalt not behold all these mysteries hidden therein.

55. The child of thy bowels, *he* shall behold them.

56. Expect him not from the East, nor from the West; for from no expected house cometh that child. Aum! All words are sacred and all prophets true; save only that they understand a little; solve the first half of the equation, leave the second unattacked. But thou hast all in the clear light, and some, though not all, in the dark.

57. Invoke me under my stars! Love is the law, love under will. Nor let the fools mistake love; for there are love and love. There is the dove, and there is the serpent. Choose ye well! He, my prophet, hath chosen, knowing the law of the fortress, and the great mystery of the House of God.

All these old letters of my Book are aright; but צ is not the Star. This also is secret: my prophet shall reveal it to the wise.

58. I give unimaginable joys on earth: certainty, not faith, while in life, upon death; peace unutterable, rest, ecstasy; nor do I demand aught in sacrifice.

59. My incense is of resinous woods & gums; and there is no blood therein: because of my hair the trees of Eternity.

60. My number is 11, as all their numbers who are of us. The Five Pointed Star, with a Circle in the Middle, & the circle is Red. My colour is black to the blind, but the blue & gold are seen of the seeing. Also I have a secret glory for them that love me.

61. But to love me is better than all things: if under the

night-stars in the desert thou presently burnest mine incense before me, invoking me with a pure heart, and the Serpent flame therein, thou shalt come a little to lie in my bosom. For one kiss wilt thou then be willing to give all; but whoso gives one particle of dust shall lose all in that hour. Ye shall gather goods and store of women and spices; ye shall wear rich jewels; ye shall exceed the nations of the earth in splendour & pride; but always in the love of me, and so shall ye come to my joy. I charge you earnestly to come before me in a single robe, and covered with a rich headdress. I love you! I yearn to you! Pale or purple, veiled or voluptuous, I who am all pleasure and purple, and drunkenness of the innermost sense, desire you. Put on the wings, and arouse the coiled splendour within you: come unto me!

62. At all my meetings with you shall the priestess say—and her eyes shall burn with desire as she stands bare and rejoicing in my secret temple—To me! To me! calling forth the flame of the hearts of all in her love-chant.

63. Sing the rapturous love-song unto me! Burn to me perfumes! Wear to me jewels! Drink to me, for I love you! I love you!

64. I am the blue-lidded daughter of Sunset; I am the naked brilliance of the voluptuous night-sky.

65. To me! To me!

66. The Manifestation of Nuit is at an end.

1. Nu! the hiding of Hadit.

2. Come! all ye, and learn the secret that hath not yet been revealed. I, Hadit, am the complement of Nu, my bride. I am not extended, and Khabs is the name of my House.

3. In the sphere I am everywhere the centre, as she, the circumference, is nowhere found.

4. Yet she shall be known & I never.

5. Behold! the rituals of the old time are black. Let the evil ones be cast away; let the good ones be purged by the prophet! Then shall this Knowledge go aright.

6. I am the flame that burns in every heart of man, and in the core of every star. I am Life, and the giver of Life, yet therefore is the knowledge of me the knowledge of death.

7. I am the Magician and the Exorcist. I am the axle of the wheel, and the cube in the circle. "Come unto me" is a foolish word: for it is I that go.

8. Who worshipped Heru-pa-kraath have worshipped me; ill, for I am the worshipper.

9. Remember all ye that existence is pure joy; that all the sorrows are but as shadows; they pass & are done; but there is that which remains.

10. O prophet! thou hast ill will to learn this writing.

11. I see thee hate the hand & the pen; but I am stronger.

12. Because of me in Thee which thou knewest not.

13. for why? Because thou wast the knower, and me.

14. Now let there be a veiling of this shrine: now let the light devour men and eat them up with blindness!

15. For I am perfect, being Not; and my number is nine by the fools; but with the just I am eight, and one in eight: Which is vital, for I am none indeed. The Empress and the King are not of me; for there is a further secret.

16. I am The Empress & the Hierophant. Thus eleven, as my bride is eleven.

17. Hear me, ye people of sighing!

The sorrows of pain and regret
Are left to the dead and the dying,
The folk that not know me as yet.

18. These are dead, these fellows; they feel not. We are not for the poor and sad: the lords of the earth are our kinsfolk.

19. Is a God to live in a dog? No! but the highest are of us. They shall rejoice, our chosen: who sorroweth is not of us.

20. Beauty and strength, leaping laughter and delicious languor, force and fire, are of us.

21. We have nothing with the outcast and the unfit: let them die in their misery. For they feel not. Compassion is the vice of kings: stamp down the wretched & the weak: this is the law of the strong: this is our law and the joy of the world. Think not, o king, upon that lie: That Thou Must Die: verily thou shalt not die, but live. Now let it be understood: If the body of the King dissolve, he shall remain in pure ecstasy for ever. Nuit! Hadit! Ra-Hoor-Khuit! The Sun, Strength & Sight, Light; these are for the servants of the Star & the Snake.

22. I am the Snake that giveth Knowledge & Delight and

bright glory, and stir the hearts of men with drunkenness. To worship me take wine and strange drugs whereof I will tell my prophet, & be drunk thereof! They shall not harm ye at all. It is a lie, this folly against self. The exposure of innocence is a lie. Be strong, o man! lust, enjoy all things of sense and rapture: fear not that any God shall deny thee for this.

23. I am alone: there is no God where I am.

24. Behold! these be grave mysteries; for there are also of my friends who be hermits. Now think not to find them in the forest or on the mountain; but in beds of purple, caressed by magnificent beasts of women with large limbs, and fire and light in their eyes, and masses of flaming hair about them; there shall ye find them. Ye shall see them at rule, at victorious armies, at all the joy; and there shall be in them a joy a million times greater than this. Beware lest any force another, King against King! Love one another with burning hearts; on the low men trample in the fierce lust of your pride, in the day of your wrath.

25. Ye are against the people, O my chosen!

26. I am the secret Serpent coiled about to spring: in my coiling there is joy. If I lift up my head, I and my Nuit are one. If I droop down mine head, and shoot forth venom, then is rapture of the earth, and I and the earth are one.

27. There is great danger in me; for who doth not understand these runes shall make a great miss. He shall fall down into the pit called Because, and there he shall perish with the dogs of Reason.

28. Now a curse upon Because and his kin!

29. May Because be accursèd for ever!

30. If Will stops and cries Why, invoking Because, then Will stops & does nought.

31. If Power asks why, then is Power weakness.

32. Also reason is a lie; for there is a factor infinite & unknown; & all their words are skew-wise.

33. Enough of Because! Be he damned for a dog!

34. But ye, o my people, rise up & awake!

35. Let the rituals be rightly performed with joy & beauty!

36. There are rituals of the elements and feasts of the times.

37. A feast for the first night of the Prophet and his Bride!

38. A feast for the three days of the writing of the Book of the Law.

39. A feast for Tahuti and the child of the Prophet—secret, O Prophet!

40. A feast for the Supreme Ritual, and a feast for the Equinox of the Gods.

41. A feast for fire and a feast for water; a feast for life and a greater feast for death!

42. A feast every day in your hearts in the joy of my rapture!

43. A feast every night unto Nu, and the pleasure of uttermost delight!

44. Aye! feast! rejoice! there is no dread hereafter. There is the dissolution, and eternal ecstasy in the kisses of Nu.

45. There is death for the dogs.

46. Dost thou fail? Art thou sorry? Is fear in thine heart?

47. Where I am these are not.

48. Pity not the fallen! I never knew them. I am not for them. I console not: I hate the consoled & the consoler.

49. I am unique & conqueror. I am not of the slaves that perish. Be they damned & dead! Amen. (This is of the 4: there is a fifth who is invisible, & therein am I as a babe in an egg.)

50. Blue am I and gold in the light of my bride: but the red gleam is in my eyes; & my spangles are purple & green.

51. Purple beyond purple: it is the light higher than eyesight.

52. There is a veil: that veil is black. It is the veil of the modest woman; it is the veil of sorrow, & the pall of death: this is none of me. Tear down that lying spectre of the centuries: veil not your vices in virtuous words: these vices are my service; ye do well, & I will reward you here and hereafter.

53. Fear not, o prophet, when these words are said, thou shalt not be sorry. Thou art emphatically my chosen; and blessed are the eyes that thou shalt look upon with gladness. But I will hide thee in a mask of sorrow: they that see thee shall fear thou art fallen: but I lift thee up.

54. Nor shall they who cry aloud their folly that thou meanest nought avail; thou shall reveal it: thou availest: they are the slaves of because: They are not of me. The stops as thou wilt; the letters? change them not in style or value!

55. Thou shalt obtain the order & value of the English Alphabet; thou shalt find new symbols to attribute them unto.

56. Begone! ye mockers; even though ye laugh in my honour ye shall laugh not long: then when ye are sad know that I have forsaken you.

57. He that is righteous shall be righteous still; he that is filthy shall be filthy still.

58. Yea! deem not of change: ye shall be as ye are, & not other. Therefore the kings of the earth shall be Kings for ever: the slaves shall serve. There is none that shall be cast down or lifted up: all is ever as it was. Yet there are masked ones my servants: it may be that yonder beggar is a King. A King may choose his garment as he will: there is no certain test: but a beggar cannot hide his poverty.

59. Beware therefore! Love all, lest perchance is a King concealed! Say you so? Fool! If he be a King, thou canst not hurt him.

60. Therefore strike hard & low, and to hell with them, master!

61. There is a light before thine eyes, o prophet, a light undesired, most desirable.

62. I am uplifted in thine heart; and the kisses of the stars rain hard upon thy body.

63. Thou art exhaust in the voluptuous fullness of the inspiration; the expiration is sweeter than death, more rapid and laughterful than a caress of Hell's own worm.

64. Oh! thou art overcome: we are upon thee; our delight is all over thee: hail! hail: prophet of Nu! prophet of Had! prophet of Ra-Hoor-Khu! Now rejoice! now come in our splendour & rapture! Come in our passionate peace, & write sweet words for the Kings!

65. I am the Master: thou art the Holy Chosen One.

66. Write, & find ecstasy in writing! Work, & be our bed in working! Thrill with the joy of life & death! Ah! thy death shall be lovely: whoso seeth it shall be glad. Thy death shall be the seal of the promise of our agelong love. Come! lift up thine heart & rejoice! We are one; we are none.

67. Hold! Hold! Bear up in thy rapture; fall not in swoon of the excellent kisses!

68. Harder! Hold up thyself! Lift thine head! breathe not so deep—die!

69. Ah! Ah! What do I feel? Is the word exhausted?

70. There is help & hope in other spells. Wisdom says: be strong! Then canst thou bear more joy. Be not animal; refine thy rapture! If thou drink, drink by the eight and ninety rules of art: if thou love, exceed by delicacy; and if thou do aught joyous, let there be subtlety therein!

71. But exceed! exceed!

72. Strive ever to more! and if thou art truly mine—and doubt it not, an if thou art ever joyous!—death is the crown of all.

73. Ah! Ah! Death! Death! thou shalt long for death. Death is forbidden, o man, unto thee.

74. The length of thy longing shall be the strength of its glory. He that lives long & desires death much is ever the King among the Kings.

75. Aye! listen to the numbers & the words:

76. 4 6 3 8 A B K 2 4 A L G M O R 3 Y X 24 89 R P S T O V A L. What meaneth this, o prophet? Thou knowest not; nor shalt thou know ever. There cometh one to follow thee: he shall expound it. But remember, o chosen

one, to be me ; to follow the love of Nu in the star-lit heaven ; to look forth upon men, to tell them this glad word.

77. O be thou proud and mighty among men !

78. Lift up thyself ! for there is none like unto thee among men or among Gods ! Lift up thyself, o my prophet, thy stature shall surpass the stars. They shall worship thy name, foursquare, mystic, wonderful, the number of the man ; and the name of thy house 418.

79. The end of the hiding of Hadit ; and blessing & worship to the prophet of the lovely Star !

1. Abrahadabra; the reward of Ra Hoor Khut.

2. There is division hither homeward; there is a word not known. Spelling is defunct; all is not aught. Beware! Hold! Raise the spell of Ra-Hoor-Khuit!

3. Now let it be first understood that I am a god of War and of Vengeance. I shall deal hardly with them.

4. Choose ye an island!

5. Fortify it!

6. Dung it about with enginery of war!

7. I will give you a war-engine.

8. With it ye shall smite the peoples; and none shall stand before you.

9. Lurk! Withdraw! Upon them! this is the Law of the Battle of Conquest: thus shall my worship be about my secret house.

10. Get the stélé of revealing itself; set it in thy secret temple—and that temple is already aright disposed—& it shall be your Kiblah for ever. It shall not fade, but miraculous colour shall come back to it day after day. Close it in locked glass for a proof to the world.

11. This shall be your only proof. I forbid argument. Conquer! That is enough. I will make easy to you the abstruction from the ill-ordered house in the Victorious City. Thou shalt thyself convey it with worship, o prophet, though thou likest it not. Thou shalt have danger & trouble. Ra-Hoor-Khu is with thee. Worship me with fire & blood; worship me with swords & with spears. Let the woman be

girt with a sword before me: let blood flow to my name. Trample down the Heathen; be upon them, o warrior, I will give you of their flesh to eat!

12. Sacrifice cattle, little and big: after a child.

13. But not now.

14. Ye shall see that hour, o blessèd Beast, and thou the Scarlet Concubine of his desire!

15. Ye shall be sad thereof.

16. Deem not too eagerly to catch the promises; fear not to undergo the curses. Ye, even ye, know not this meaning all.

17. Fear not at all; fear neither men nor Fates, nor gods, nor anything. Money fear not, nor laughter of the folk folly, nor any other power in heaven or upon the earth or under the earth. Nu is your refuge as Hadit your light; and I am the strength, force, vigour, of your arms.

18. Mercy let be off: damn them who pity! Kill and torture; spare not; be upon them!

19. That stélé they shall call the Abomination of Desolation; count well its name, & it shall be to you as 718.

20. Why? Because of the fall of Because, that he is not there again.

21. Set up my image in the East: thou shalt buy thee an image which I will show thee, especial, not unlike the one thou knowest. And it shall be suddenly easy for thee to do this.

22. The other images group around me to support me: let all be worshipped, for they shall cluster to exalt me. I am the visible object of worship; the others are secret; for the Beast & his Bride are they: and for the winners of the Ordeal x. What is this? Thou shalt know.

23. For perfume mix meal & honey & thick leavings of red wine: then oil of Abramelin and olive oil, and afterward soften & smooth down with rich fresh blood.

24. The best blood is of the moon, monthly: then the fresh blood of a child, or dropping from the host of heaven: then of enemies; then of the priest or of the worshippers: last of some beast, no matter what.

25. This burn: of this make cakes & eat unto me. This hath also another use; let it be laid before me, and kept thick with perfumes of your orison: it shall become full of beetles as it were and creeping things sacred unto me.

26. These slay, naming your enemies; & they shall fall before you.

27. Also these shall breed lust & power of lust in you at the eating thereof.

28. Also ye shall be strong in war.

29. Moreover, be they long kept, it is better; for they swell with my force. All before me.

30. My altar is of open brass work: burn thereon in silver or gold!

31. There cometh a rich man from the West who shall pour his gold upon thee.

32. From gold forge steel!

33. Be ready to fly or to smite!

34. But your holy place shall be untouched throughout the centuries: though with fire and sword it be burnt down & shattered, yet an invisible house there standeth, and shall stand until the fall of the Great Equinox; when Hrumachis shall arise and the double-wanded one assume my throne and place. Another prophet shall arise, and bring fresh fever

from the skies; another woman shall awake the lust & worship of the Snake; another soul of God and beast shall mingle in the globèd priest; another sacrifice shall stain the tomb; another king shall reign; and blessing no longer be poured To the Hawk-headed mystical Lord!

35. The half of the word of Heru-ra-ha, called Hoor-pa-kraat and Ra-Hoor-Khut.

36. Then said the prophet unto the God:

37. I adore thee in the song—

I am the Lord of Thebes, and I
  The inspired forth-speaker of Mentu;
For me unveils the veilèd sky,
  The self-slain Ankh-af-na-khonsu
Whose words are truth. I invoke, I greet
  Thy presence, O Ra-Hoor-Khuit!

Unity uttermost showed!
  I adore the might of Thy breath,
Supreme and terrible God,
  Who makest the gods and death
To tremble before Thee:—
  I, I adore thee!

Appear on the throne of Ra!
  Open the ways of the Khu!
Lighten the ways of the Ka!
  The ways of the Khabs run through
To stir me or still me!
  Aum! let it fill me!

38. So that thy light is in me; & its red flame is as a sword in my hand to push thy order. There is a secret door that I shall make to establish thy way in all the quarters, (these are the adorations, as thou hast written), as it is said:

> The light is mine; its rays consume
> Me: I have made a secret door
> Into the House of Ra and Tum,
> Of Khephra and of Ahathoor.
> I am thy Theban, O Mentu,
> The prophet Ankh-af-na-khonsu!
>
> By Bes-na-Maut my breast I beat;
> By wise Ta-Nech I weave my spell.
> Show thy star-splendour, O Nuit!
> Bid me within thine House to dwell,
> O wingèd snake of light, Hadit!
> Abide with me, Ra-Hoor-Khuit!

39. All this and a book to say how thou didst come hither and a reproduction of this ink and paper for ever—for in it is the word secret & not only in the English—and thy comment upon this the Book of the Law shall be printed beautifully in red ink and black upon beautiful paper made by hand; and to each man and woman that thou meetest, were it but to dine or to drink at them, it is the Law to give. Then they shall chance to abide in this bliss or no; it is no odds. Do this quickly!

40. But the work of the comment? That is easy; and

Hadit burning in thy heart shall make swift and secure thy pen.

41. Establish at thy Kaaba a clerk-house: all must be done well and with business way.

42. The ordeals thou shalt oversee thyself, save only the blind ones. Refuse none, but thou shalt know & destroy the traitors. I am Ra-Hoor-Khuit; and I am powerful to protect my servant. Success is thy proof: argue not; convert not; talk not overmuch! Them that seek to entrap thee, to overthrow thee, them attack without pity or quarter; & destroy them utterly. Swift as a trodden serpent turn and strike! Be thou yet deadlier than he! Drag down their souls to awful torment: laugh at their fear: spit upon them!

43. Let the Scarlet Woman beware! If pity and compassion and tenderness visit her heart; if she leave my work to toy with old sweetnesses; then shall my vengeance be known. I will slay me her child: I will alienate her heart: I will cast her out from men: as a shrinking and despised harlot shall she crawl through dusk wet streets, and die cold and an-hungered.

44. But let her raise herself in pride! Let her follow me in my way! Let her work the work of wickedness! Let her kill her heart! Let her be loud and adulterous! Let her be covered with jewels, and rich garments, and let her be shameless before all men!

45. Then will I lift her to pinnacles of power: then will I breed from her a child mightier than all the kings of the earth. I will fill her with joy: with my force shall she see & strike at the worship of Nu: she shall achieve Hadit.

46. I am the warrior Lord of the Forties: the Eighties

cower before me, & are abased. I will bring you to victory & joy: I will be at your arms in battle & ye shall delight to slay. Success is your proof; courage is your armour; go on, go on, in my strength; & ye shall turn not back for any!

47. This book shall be translated into all tongues: but always with the original in the writing of the Beast; for in the chance shape of the letters and their position to one another: in these are mysteries that no Beast shall divine. Let him not seek to try: but one cometh after him, whence I say not, who shall discover the Key of it all. Then this line drawn is a key: then this circle squared in its failure is a key also. And Abrahadabra. It shall be his child & that strangely. Let him not seek after this; for thereby alone can he fall from it.

48. Now this mystery of the letters is done, and I want to go on to the holier place.

49. I am in a secret fourfold word, the blasphemy against all gods of men.

50. Curse them! Curse them! Curse them!

51. With my Hawk's head I peck at the eyes of Jesus as he hangs upon the cross.

52. I flap my wings in the face of Mohammed & blind him.

53. With my claws I tear out the flesh of the Indian and the Buddhist, Mongol and Din.

54. Bahlasti! Ompehda! I spit on your crapulous creeds.

55. Let Mary inviolate be torn upon wheels: for her sake let all chaste women be utterly despised among you!

56. Also for beauty's sake and love's!

57. Despise also all cowards; professional soldiers who dare not fight, but play; all fools despise!

58. But the keen and the proud, the royal and the lofty; ye are brothers!

59. As brothers fight ye!

60. There is no law beyond Do what thou wilt.

61. There is an end of the word of the God enthroned in Ra's seat, lightening the girders of the soul.

62. To Me do ye reverence! to me come ye through tribulation of ordeal, which is bliss.

63. The fool readeth this Book of the Law, and its comment; & he understandeth it not.

64. Let him come through the first ordeal, & it will be to him as silver.

65. Through the second, gold.

66. Through the third, stones of precious water.

67. Through the fourth, ultimate sparks of the intimate fire.

68. Yet to all it shall seem beautiful. Its enemies who say not so, are mere liars.

69. There is success.

70. I am the Hawk-Headed Lord of Silence & of Strength; my nemyss shrouds the night-blue sky.

71. Hail! ye twin warriors about the pillars of the world! for your time is nigh at hand.

72. I am the Lord of the Double Wand of Power; the wand of the Force of Coph Nia—but my left hand is empty, for I have crushed an Universe; & nought remains.

73. Paste the sheets from right to left and from top to bottom: then behold!

74. There is a splendour in my name hidden and glorious, as the sun of midnight is ever the son.

75. The ending of the words is the Word Abrahadabra.

The Book of the Law is Written
and Concealed.
Aum. Ha.

(For doubtful spellings and styles consult facsimile MS. at the end of this volume.)

GENESIS
LIBRI
AL

A∴A∴ Publication in Class B.

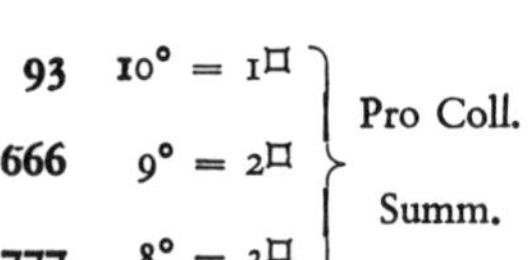

V. N.	Præmonstrator	Pro Coll. Ext.
P.	Imperator	
Achad.	Cancellarius	

I. W. E.	7° = 4□	Pro Coll. Int.
O. M.	7° = 4□	
O. S. V.	6° = 5□	
Parsival.	5° = 6□	

GENESIS LIBRI AL

CHAPTER I.[1]

The Boyhood of Aleister Crowley.

AT 36 Clarendon Square, Leamington, Warwickshire, England, at 10.50 p.m. on the twelfth day of October, in the Eighteen Hundred and Seventy-Fifth Year of the vulgar era, was born the person whose history is to be recounted.

His father was named Edward Crowley; his mother, Emily Bertha, her maiden name being Bishop. Edward Crowley was an Exclusive Plymouth Brother, the most considered leader in that sect. This branch of the family of Crowley has been settled in England since Tudor times, but is Celtic in origin, Crowley being a clan in Kerry and other counties in the South-West of Ireland, of the same stock as the Breton 'de Querouaille' or 'de Kerval' which gave a Duchess of Portsmouth to England. It is supposed that the English branch—the direct ancestry of Edward Alexander Crowley—came to England with the Duke of Richmond, and took root at Bosworth.

[1] In the Book of the Law we find in the 3rd chapter and the 39th to the 41st verse an instruction to issue a book to say how this Revelation was obtained, with certain details with regard to the style in which it is to be done.

It has hitherto been impossible to comply with this injunction, although an attempt was made in "The Temple of Solomon the King". We now proceed to do so; the subject divides itself into Eight Chapters.—[Ed.]

In 1881 he went to live at The Grange, Redhill, Surrey. In 1884 the boy, who had till then been educated by governesses and tutors, was sent to a school at St. Leonards, kept by some extreme Evangelicals named Habershon. A year later he was transferred to a school at Cambridge kept by a Plymouth Brother of the name of Champney. (The dates in this paragraph are possibly inaccurate. Documentary evidence is at the present moment unavailable. Ed.)

On March 5, 1887, Edward Crowley died. Two years later the boy was removed from the school. Those two years were years of unheard-of torture. He has written details in the Preface to "The World's Tragedy." This torture seriously undermined his health. For two years he travelled, mostly in Wales and Scotland, with tutors. In 1890 he went for a short time to a school at Streatham, kept by a man named Yarrow, his mother having moved there in order to be near her brother, an extremely narrow Evangelical named Tom Bond Bishop. This prepared him for Malvern, which he entered at the summer term of 1891. He only remained there a year, as his health was still very delicate. In the autumn he entered for a term at Tonbridge, but fell seriously ill, and had to be removed. The year 1893 was spent with tutors, principally in Wales, the north of Scotland, and Eastbourne. In 1895 he completed his studies in chemistry at King's College, London, and in October of that year entered Trinity College, Cambridge.

With this ends the first period of his life. It is only necessary to state briefly that his brain developed early. At four years old he could read the Bible aloud, showing a marked predilection for the lists of long names, the only part of the Bible which has not been tampered with by theologians.[1] He could also play chess well enough to beat the average amateur, and though constantly playing never lost a game till 1895.[2] He was taught by a tailor who had been summoned to make clothes for his father, and was treated as a guest on account of his being a fellow " Plymouth Brother ". He beat his teacher uniformly after the first game. He must have been six or seven years old at this time.

He began to write poetry in 1886, if not earlier. Vide " Oracles ".

After the death of his father, who was a man of strong common sense, and never allowed his religion to interfere with natural affection, he was in the hands of people of an entirely contrary disposition. His mental attitude was soon concentrated in hatred of the religion which they taught, and his will concentrated in revolt against its oppressions. His main method of relief was mountaineering, which left him alone with nature, away from the tyrants.

The years from March, 1887, until entering Trinity College, Cambridge, in October, 1895, represented a continual struggle towards freedom. At Cambridge he felt himself to be his own master, refused to attend Chapel, Lectures or Hall, and was wisely left alone to work out his own salvation by his tutor, the late Dr. A. W. Verrall.

[1] This curious trait may perhaps be evidence of his poetical feeling, his passion for the bizarre and mysterious, or even of his aptitude for the Hebrew Qabalah. It may also be interpreted as a clue to his magical ancestry.

[2] The first man to beat him was H. E. Atkins, British Chess Champion (Amateur) for many years.

It must be stated that he possessed natural intellectual ability to an altogether extraordinary degree. He had the faculty of memory, especially verbal memory, in astonishing perfection.

As a boy he could find almost any verse in the Bible after a few minutes search. In 1900 he was tested in the works of Shakespeare, Shelley, Swinburne (1st series of Poems and Ballads), Browning and The Moonstone. He was able to place exactly any phrase from any of these books, and in nearly every case to continue with the passage.

He showed remarkable facility in acquiring the elements of Latin, Greek, French, Mathematics and Science. He learnt "little Roscoe" almost by heart, on his own initiative. When in the Lower Fifth at Malvern, he came out sixth in the school in the annual Shakespeare examination, though he had given only two days to preparing for it. Once, when the Mathematical Master, wishing to devote the hour to cramming advanced pupils, told the class to work out a set of examples of Quadratic Equations, he retorted by asking at the end of forty minutes what he should do next, and handed up the whole series of 63 equations, correct.

He passed all his examinations both at school and university with honours, though refusing uniformly to work for them.

On the other hand, he could not be persuaded or constrained to apply himself to any subject which did not appeal to him. He showed intense repugnance to history, geography, and botany, among others. He could never learn to write Greek and Latin verses, this probably because the rules of scansion seemed arbitrary and formal.

Again, it was impossible to him to take interest in anything from the moment that he had grasped the principles of "how it was, or might be, done." This trait prevented him from putting the finishing touches to anything he attempted.

For instance, he refused to present himself for the second part of his final examination for his B.A. degree, simply because he knew himself thoroughly master of the subject ![1]

This characteristic extended to his physical pleasures. He was abjectly incompetent at easy practice climbing on boulders, because he knew he could do them. It seemed incredible to the other men that this lazy duffer should be the most daring and dexterous cragsman of his generation, as he proved himself whenever he tackled a precipice which had baffled every other climber in the world.[2] Similarly, once he had worked out theoretically a method of climbing a mountain, he was quite content to tell the secret to others, and let them appropriate the glory. (The first ascent of the Dent du Géant from the Montanvers is a case in point.) It mattered everything to him that something should be done, nothing that he should be the one to do it.

This almost inhuman unselfishness was not incompatible with consuming and insatiable personal ambition. The key to the puzzle is probably this; he wanted to be something that nobody else had ever been, or could be. He lost interest in chess as soon as he had proved to himself (at the age of 22) that he was a master of the game, having beaten some of the strongest amateurs in England, and even one or two professional "masters." He turned from poetry to painting, more or

1 Swinburne similarly refused to be examined in Classics at Oxford on the ground that he knew more than the examiners.

2 In Chess also he has beaten many International Masters, and ranks on the Continent as a Minor Master himself. But he cannot be relied upon to win against a second-rate player in a Club Match.

less, when he had made it quite certain that he was the greatest poet of his time. Even in Magick, having become The Word of the Aeon, and thus taken his place with the other Seven Magi known to history, out of reach of all possible competition, he began to neglect the subject. He is only able to devote himself to it as he does because he has eliminated all personal ideas from his Work; it has become as automatic as respiration.

We must also put on record his extraordinary powers in certain unusual spheres. He can remember the minutest details of a rock-climb, after years of absence. He can retrace his steps over any path once traversed, in the wildest weather or the blackest night. He can divine the one possible passage through the most complex and dangerous ice-fall. (E.g. the Vuibez séracs in 1897, the Mer de Glace, right centre, in 1899).

He possesses a "sense of direction" independent of any known physical methods of taking one's bearings; and this is as effective in strange cities as on mountains or deserts. He can smell the presence of water, of snow, and other supposedly scentless substances. His endurance is exceptional. He has been known to write for 67 consecutive hours: his "Tannhäuser" was thus written in 1900. He has walked over 100 miles in 2½ days, in the desert: as in the winter of 1910. He has frequently made expeditions lasting over 36 hours, on mountains, in the most adverse conditions. He holds the World's record for the greatest number of days spent on a glacier—65 days on the Baltoro in 1902; also that for the greatest pace uphill over 16,000 feet—4,000 feet in 1 hour 23 minutes on Iztaccihuatl in 1900; that for the highest peak (first ascent by a solitary climber)—the Nevado de Toluca in 1901; and numerous others.[1]

Yet he is utterly fagged-out by the mere idea of a walk of a few hundred yards, if it does not interest him, and excite his imagination, to take it; and it is only with the greatest effort that he can summon the energy to write a few lines if, instead of his wanting to do them, he merely knows that they must be done.

This account has been deemed necessary to explain how it is that a man of such unimaginably commanding qualities as to have made him world-famous in so many diverse spheres of action, should have been so grotesquely unable to make use of his faculties, or even of his achievements, in any of the ordinary channels of human activity; to consolidate his personal pre-eminence, or even to secure his position from a social or economic standpoint.

[1] Written in 1920 e.v.: these records may no longer stand.

CHAPTER II.

Adolescence: Beginnings of Magick.

The Birth of FRATER PERDURABO.

$0^{\circ}=0^{\square}$ to $4^{\circ}=7^{\square}$

HAVING won freedom, he had the sense not to waste any time in enjoying it. He had been deprived of all English literature but the Bible during the whole of his youth, and he spent his three years at Cambridge in repairing the defect. He was also working for the Diplomatic Service, the late Lord Salisbury and the late Lord Ritchie having taken an interest in his career, and given him nominations. In October, 1897, he was suddenly recalled to his understanding of the evils of the alleged 'existing religion,' and experienced a trance, in which he perceived the utter folly of all human ambition. The fame of an ambassador rarely outlives a century. That of a poet is almost as ephemeral. The earth must one day perish. He must build in some material more lasting. This conception drove him to the study of Alchemy and Magick. He wrote to the author of "The Book of Black Magic and of Pacts," a pompous American named Arthur Waite, notorious for the affectations and obscurities of his style, and the mealy-mouthed muddle of his mysticism. This nebulous impresario, presenting an asthmatic Isis in the Opera "Bull-Frogs," had hinted in his preface that he knew certain occult sanctuaries wherein Truth and Wisdom were jealously guarded by a body of Initiates, to be dispensed to the postulant who proved himself worthy to partake of their privileges. Mr. Waite recommended him to read a book called "The Cloud on the Sanctuary."

His taste for mountaineering had become a powerful passion, and he was climbing in Cumberland when he met Oscar Eckenstein, perhaps the greatest of all the mountaineers of his period, with whom he was destined to climb thenceforward until 1902.

In the summer a party was formed to camp on the Schönbuhl Glacier at the foot of the Dent Blanche, with a view to an expedition to the Himalayas later on. During his weeks on the Glacier, where the bad weather was continuous, he studied assiduously the translation by S. L. Mathers of three books which form part of von Rosenroth's "Kabbalah Unveiled." On one of his descents to Zermatt, he met a distinguished chemist, Julian L. Baker, who had studied Alchemy. He hunted this clue through the valley, and made Baker promise to meet him in London at the end of the season, and introduce him to others who were interested in Occult science. This happened in September; through Baker, he met another chemist named George Cecil Jones, who introduced him to the Hermetic Order of the Golden Dawn. He made rapid progress in this Order, and in the spring of 1900 was its chief in England. The details of this period must be studied in "The Temple of Solomon the King," where a full account of the Order is given. In the Order he met one, Allan Bennett, Frater Iehi Aour. Jones and Bennett were both Adepts of high standing. The latter came to live with him in his flat, and together they carried out many operations of ceremonial magick. Allan Bennett was in constant ill-health, and went to Ceylon at the end of 1899. It was on his entry into this Order that the subject of this history took the motto of " Perdurabo "—'I will endure to the end.'

In July, 1900, he went to Mexico, and devoted his whole time to the continued practice of Magick, in which he obtained extraordinary success. (See Equinox Vol. I, No. III for a condensed account of some of these. It may be here stated summarily that he invoked certain Gods, Goddesses, and Spirits to visible appearance, learnt how to heal physical and moral diseases, how to make himself invisible, how to obtain communications from spiritual sources, how to control other minds, etc., etc.) And then . . . .

CHAPTER III.

Beginnings of Mysticism.

The Birth of FRATER OU MH.

$7^{\circ}=4^{\square}$

OSCAR ECKENSTEIN, on his arrival in Mexico, where he was to climb mountains with the subject of our essay, found him in a rather despondent mood. He had attained the most satisfactory results. He was able to communicate with the divine forces, and operations such as those of invisibility and evocation had been mastered. Yet with all this there was a certain dissatisfaction. Success had not given him all that he had hoped for. He placed the situation before his companion, rather to clear his own mind than hoping for any help, for he supposed him to be entirely ignorant of all these subjects, which he habitually treated with dislike and contempt. Judge of his surprise, then, when he found in this unpromising quarter a messenger from the Great White Brotherhood! His companion told him to abandon all magick.

" The Task," said Eckenstein, " involves the control of the mind. Yours is a wandering mind." The proposition was indignantly denied.

" Test it," said the Master.

A short experiment was conclusive. It was impossible for

the boy to keep his mind fixed upon a single object for even a few seconds at a time. The mind, though perfectly stable in motion, was unable to rest, just as a gyroscope falls when the flywheel slows down. An entirely new course of experiments was consequently undertaken. Half-an-hour every morning and half-an-hour every evening were devoted to attempts to control the mind, by the simple process of imagining a familiar object, and endeavouring to keep concentrated upon it.[1]

He soon became sufficiently expert in this initial practice to proceed to concentration on regularly moving objects such as a pendulum, and, ultimately, on living objects. A further series of experiments dealt with the other senses. He tried to imagine and retain the taste of chocolate or of quinine, the smell of various familiar perfumes, the sound of bells, waterfalls, and so on, or the feeling excited by such objects as velvet, silk, fur, sand and steel.

In the spring of 1901, he left Mexico, went to San Francisco, Honolulu, Japan, China and Ceylon, always continuing these experiments. His Master had not told him to what they would ultimately lead. In Ceylon he found Frater I.A. (Allan Bennett), with whom he went to Kandy, where they took a bungalow named Marlborough, overlooking the lake.

I.A. had himself been developing on similar lines under P. Ramanathan, the Solicitor-General of Ceylon, known to occultists under the name of Shri Parananda.[2] I.A. told him that in order to concentrate he must first see that no interrup-

[1] See Part I of Book 4 for a description of this, and an explanation of the difficulty of the task, even in the case of one whose powers of concentrated attention, in the ordinary sense of the phrase, are highly developed.

[2] He is the author of commentaries on the Gospels of Matthew and John, which he explains as containing many of the aphorisms of Yoga.

tions reached him from the body, and counselled the adoption of Asana, a settled position in which all bodily movement was to be suppressed. Further, he was to practice Pranayama, or control of the breathing, which has a similar effect in reducing to the lowest possible point the internal movements of the body.[1]

During the months of this stay at Kandy, he practised these, obtained success in Asana, the intense pain of the practices being overcome, and changed into an indescribable sense of physical well-being and comfort.

While in Pranayama he passed through the first stage, which is marked by profuse perspiration of a peculiar kind; the second, which is accompanied by rigidity of the body; and the third, in which the body unconsciously hops about the floor, without in any way disturbing the Asana.

During the latter part of August and the whole of September, his practices became continuous by day and night, in order to create a rhythm in the mind similar to that which Pranayama produces in the body. He adopted a Mantra, or sacred sentence, by the constant repetition of which it became automatic in his brain, so that it would continue through sleep, and he would wake up actually repeating the words. Sleep itself, too, was broken up into short periods of very light sleep of a peculiar kind, in which consciousness is hardly lost, although the body obtains perfect rest. These practices continued into October, at the beginning of which he reached the state of Dhyana, a tremendous spiritual experience, in which the subject and object of meditation unite with excessive violence in

[1] See Part I of Book 4 for full descriptions, and Equinox Vol. I, No. 4 for some of FRATER PERDURABO'S records of these practices.

blinding brilliance and music of a kind to which earthly harmony affords no parallel.[1]

The result of this however was to cause so intense a satisfaction with his progress, that he gave up work. He then visited Anuradhapura and others of the buried cities of Ceylon. In November he went to India, and in January visited I.A. at Akyab in Burma, where that Adept was living in a monastery, with the intention of preparing himself to take the Yellow Robe of the Buddhist Sangha. The whole of the summer of 1902 was spent in an expedition to Chogo Ri (K2) in the Himalayas.[2] During the whole of this period he did very little occult work.

November, 1902, found him in Paris, where he stayed off and on till the spring of 1903, when he returned to his house in Scotland.

We must now go backwards in time, to take up a thread which had run through his whole work, so important as to demand a chapter to itself:—

[1] See Part I of Book 4, and Equinox Vol. I, No. IV.

[2] An account of this journey is given by Dr. Jacot-Guillarmod : " Six mois dans l'Himalaya." His own story is in " The Spirit of Solitude " (The Confessions of Aleister Crowley) Vol. II.

CHAPTER IV.

The Sacred Magic of Abramelin the Mage.

The Birth of

FRATER———[1]5°=6□ *A∴A∴*

IN the autumn of 1898 George Cecil Jones had directed the attention of Frater Perdurabo to a book entitled "The Book of the Sacred Magic of Abramelin the Mage." The essence of this book is as follows:

The aspirant must have a house secure from observation and interference. In this house there must be an oratory with a window to the East, and a door to the North opening upon a terrace, at the end of which must be a lodge. He must have a Robe, Crown, Wand, Altar, Incense, Anointing Oil, and a Silver Lamen. The terrace and lodge must be strewn with fine sand. He withdraws himself gradually from human intercourse to devote himself more and more to prayer for the space of four months. He must then occupy two months in almost continuous prayer, speaking as little as possible to anybody. At the end of this period he invokes a being described as the Holy Guardian Angel, who appears to him (or to a child employed by him), and who will write in dew upon the Lamen, which is placed upon the Altar. The Oratory is filled with Divine Perfume not of the aspirant's kindling.

[1] The Mystic Name of an Adept of this degree is not to be divulged without special reasons for so doing.

After a period of communion with the Angel, he summons the Four Great Princes of the Daemonic World, and forces them to swear obedience.

On the following day he calls forward and subdues the Eight Sub-Princes; and the day after that, the many Spirits serving these. These inferior Daemons, of whom four act as familiar spirits, then operate a collection of talismans for various purposes. Such is a brief account of the Operation described in the book.

This Operation strongly appealed to our student. He immediately set about to procure a suitable house, and to prepare everything that might be necessary for the operation. All was ready for the beginning in Easter of 1900, and it must be said that the preliminary work alone is so tremendous that a long story might be written of the events of these 18 months of preparation. The Operation itself was however never begun. A fortnight or so before the time appointed, he received an urgent appeal from his Master to save him and the Order from destruction. He gave up his own prospects of personal advancement without hesitation, and hastened to Paris.[1]

That the Master proved to be no Master, and the Order no Order, but the incarnation of Disorder, had no effect upon the good Karma created by this renunciation of a project on which he had set his heart for so long.

In Mexico, he kept vigil during several nights in the Temple of the Order of the Lamp of the Invisible Light, an Order whose High Priest is pledged to maintain a Secret and Eternal Lamp. In this shrine he received some shadowing forth of

[1] See the Equinox "The Temple of Solomon the King" for a fairly full account of these various matters. The "Master" was the late S. L. Mathers.

the Vision of the Holy Guardian Angel, and that of the Four Great Princes: here also he renewed the Oath of the Operation.

(The whole of his magical career is best interpreted as the performance of this Operation. One must not suppose that Initiation is a formality, observing the "unities," like being made a Mason. All life pertains to the process, and it pervades the whole personality; the official recognition of attainment is merely a token of what has taken place.)

On his return to Scotland in 1903, he found ample evidence of the presence of the forces of the Operation, but by now, having conceived that Work in a subtler manner and having prepared to carry it out in the Temple of his own body, having seen Magick, in short, more or less in the manner in which it is seen in Parts II and III of the Book 4, he was able to dispense with the exterior physical appurtenances of this Operation.

We must now pass over a few years, and deal with the completion of this Operation, although it is in a sense irrelevant to the purpose of this book.

During the winter of 1905-6, he was travelling across China. He had come to the point of conquering his mind. That mind had broken up. He saw that the human mind is by its very nature evanescent, because of the fact that nature is not unity but duality. Truth is relative. All things end in mystery. In such sentences have the philosophers of the past formulated this proposition, as announcing the intellectual bankruptcy which he, with greater frankness, describes as insanity.

Passing from this, he became as a little child, and on reaching the Unity behind the mind, found the purpose of his life formulated in these words, *The Obtaining of the Knowledge and Conversation of the Holy Guardian Angel.*

He then found himself, having destroyed all other Karma, perfectly free to pursue this one work. He then accomplished the six months of Invocation, as prescribed in the Book of the Sacred Magic, and was rewarded in October, 1906, by complete success.[1]

He then proceeded to the evocation and conquest of the Four Great Princes and their Inferiors, a work whose results must be studied in the light of his subsequent career.

We have now finished all that is necessary to say concerning him, for the account of some of his further Attainment is given fully in Liber CDXVIII, "The Vision and the Voice," also in Equinox Vol. I No. X "The Temple of Solomon the King," where the unexpected result of the Communion of the Holy Guardian Angel is shown in a symbolism which can hardly be understood without reference to the events of 1904, which are now wholly pertinent to this Essay.

[1] An account of these matters, in part, is to be found in the Equinox, Vol. I, No. VIII, and in his own poem "Aha!"

CHAPTER V.

The Results of Recession.

THE wisest of the Popes, on being shown some miracles, refused to be impressed, remarking that he did not believe in them, he had seen too many. The result of the Meditation practices and their results, following those of Magick, was to give our student a conception of the Universe which was purely mental. Everything was a phenomenon in mind. He did not as yet see that this conception is self-destructive; but it made him sceptical, and indifferent to whatever happened. You cannot really be impressed by anything which you know to be nothing more than one of your own thoughts. Any occurrence can be interpreted as a thought, or as a relation between two thoughts. In practice this leads to profound indifferentism, miracles having become commonplace. But what would be the amazement of the priest who, placing the Host upon his tongue, found his mouth full of bleeding flesh! At the period of writing, it is evident for what purpose our student was led into this state. It was not to the Magician, not to the mystic, it was to a militant member of the Rationalist Press Association that the great Revelation was to be made. It was necessary to prove to him that there was in actual truth a Sanctuary, that there was in sober earnest a body of Adepts. It matters nothing whether these Adepts are incarnated or discarnated, human or divine. The only point at issue is that

E

there should be conscious Beings in possession of the deepest secrets of Nature, pledged to the uplifting of humanity, filled with Truth, Wisdom and Understanding. It is practical to prove the existence of individuals whose knowledge and power, although not complete—for the nature of Knowledge and Power is such that they can never be complete, since the ideas themselves contain imperfections—are yet enormously greater than aught known to the rest of humanity.

It was of such a body that our student had heard in the "Cloud upon the Sanctuary"; admission to its adyta had been the guiding hope of his life. His early attainments had tended rather to shake his belief in the existence of such an organization. He had not yet reckoned up the events of his life; he had not yet divined the direction and the set purpose informing their apparently vagrant course. It might have been by chance that whenever he had been confronted with any difficulty the right person had instantly come forward to solve it, whether in the valleys of Switzerland, the mountains of Mexico, or the jungles of the East.

At this period of his life he would have scouted the idea as fantastic. He had yet to learn that the story of Balaam and his prophetic ass might be literally true. For the great Message that came to him came, not through the mouth of any person with any pretensions to any knowledge of this or any other sort, but through an empty-headed woman of society. The plain facts of this revelation must be succinctly stated in a new chapter.

CHAPTER VI.

The Great Revelation.

The Arising of
THE BEAST 666.

$9^{\circ}=2^{\square}$

IT has been judged best to reprint as it stands the account of these matters originally compiled for " The Temple of Solomon the King." (Equinox Vol. I, No. VII, pp 357-386.)[1]

THE PRIEST.

In opening this the most important section of Frater P.'s career, we may be met by the unthinking with the criticism that since it deals rather with his relation to others than with his personal attainment, it has no place in this volume.[2]

Such criticism is indeed shallow. True, the incidents which we are about to record took place on planes material or contiguous thereto; true, so obscure is the light by which we walk that much must be left in doubt; true, we have not as yet the supreme mystical attainment to record; but on the other hand it is our view that the Seal set upon Attainment may be itself fittingly recorded in the story of that Attainment,

[1] The notes for this article were worked out in collaboration with Captain (now Major-General) J. F. C. Fuller. Every means of cross-examination was pressed to the utmost.

[2] Projected by Fuller as no more than a record of the personal attainment of Aleister Crowley.

and that no step in progress is more important than that when it is said to the aspirant: "Now that you are able to walk alone, let it be your first care to use that strength to help others!" And so this great event which we are about to describe, an event which will lead, as time will show, to the establishment of a New Heaven and a New Earth for all men, wore the simplest and humblest guise. So often the gods come clad as peasants or as children; nay, I have listened to their voices in stones and trees.

However, we must not forget that there are persons so sensitive and so credulous that they are convinced by anything, I suppose that there are nearly as many beds in the world as there are men; yet for the Evangelical every bed conceals its Jesuit. We get "Milton composing baby rhymes" and "Locke reasoning in gibberish," divine revelations which would shock the intelligence of a sheep or a Saxon; and we find these upheld and defended with skill and courage.

Therefore, since we are to announce the divine revelation made to Fra. P., it is of the last importance that we should study his mind as it was at the time of the Unveiling. If we find it to be the mind of a neurotic, of a mystic, of a person predisposed, we shall slight the revelation; if it be that of a sane man of the world, we shall attach more importance to it.

If some dingy Alchemist emerges from his laboratory, and proclaims to all Tooting that he has made gold, men doubt; but the conversion to spiritualism of Professor Lombroso made a great deal of impression on those who did not understand that his criminology was but the heaped delusion of a diseased brain.

So we shall find that the A.·.A.·. subtly prepared Fra. P. by over two years' training in rationalism and indifferentism for Their message. And we shall find that so well did They do Their work that he refused the message for five years more, in spite of many strange proofs of its truth. We shall find even that Fra. P. had to be stripped naked of himself before he could effectively deliver the message.

The battle was between all that mighty will of his and the Voice of a Brother who spoke once, and entered again into His silence ; and it was not Fra. P. who had the victory.

We left Fra. P. in the autumn of 1901 having made considerable progress in Yoga. We noted that in 1902 he did little or nothing either in Magic or Mysticism. The interpretation of the occult phenomena which he had observed occupied him exclusively, and his mind was more and more attracted to materialism.

What are phenomena ? he asked. Of noumena I know and can know nothing. All I know is, as far as I know, a mere modification of the mind, a phase of consciousness. And thought is a secretion of the brain. Consciousness is a function of the brain.

If this thought was contradicted by the obvious, " And what is the brain ? A phenomenon in mind ! ", it weighed less with him. It seemed to his mind as yet unbalanced (for all men are unbalanced until they have crossed the Abyss), that it was more important to insist on matter than on mind. Idealism wrought such misery, was the father of all illusion, never led to research. And yet, what odds ? Every act or thought is determined by an infinity of causes, is the resultant of an infinity of forces. He analysed God, saw that every man had made God in his own image, saw the savage and cannibal

Jews devoted to a savage and cannibal God, who commanded the rape of virgins and the murder of little children. He saw the timid inhabitants of India, races continually the prey of every robber tribe, inventing the effeminate Vishnu; while, under the same name, their conquerors worshipped a warrior, the conqueror of Demon Swans. He saw the flower of the earth throughout all time, the gracious Greeks, what gracious gods they had invented. He saw Rome, in its strength devoted to Mars, Jupiter and Hercules, in its decay turning to emasculate Attis, slain Adonis, murdered Osiris, crucified Christ. He could even trace in his own life every aspiration, every devotion, as a reflection of his physical and intellectual needs. He saw, too, the folly of all this supernaturalism. He heard the Boers and the British pray to the same Protestant God, and it occurred to him that the early success of the former might be due rather to superior valour than to superior praying power, and their eventual defeat to the circumstance that they could only bring 60,000 men against a quarter of a million. He saw, too, the face of humanity mired in its own blood that dripped from the leeches of religion fastened to its temples.

In all this he saw man as the only thing worth holding to; the one thing that needed to be "saved," but also the one thing that could save it.

All that he had attained, then, he abandoned. The intuitions of the Qabalah were cast behind him with a smile at his youthful folly; magic, if true, led nowhere; Yoga had become psychology. For the solution of his original problems of the universe he looked to metaphysics; he devoted his intellect to the cult of absolute reason. He took up once more with Kant, Hume, Spencer, Huxley, Tyndall, Maudsley, Mansel, Fichte, Schelling, Hegel, and many another; while as for his life, was he not a man? He had a wife; he knew his duty to the race, and to his own ancient graft thereof. He was a traveller and a sportsman; very well, then, live it! So we find that from November, 1901 he did no practices of any kind until the Spring Equinox of 1904, with the exception of a casual week in the summer of 1903, and an exhibition game of magick in the King's Chamber of the Great Pyramid in November, 1903, when by his invocations he filled that chamber with a brightness as of full moonlight. (This was no subjective illusion. The light was sufficient for him to read the ritual by.) Only to conclude, "There, you see it? What's the good of it?"

We find him climbing mountains, skating, fishing, hunting big game, fulfilling the duties of a husband; we find him with the antipathy to all forms of spiritual thought and work which marks disappointment.

If one goes up the wrong mountain by mistake, as may happen, no beauties of that mountain can compensate for the disillusionment when the error is laid bare. Leah may have been a very nice girl indeed, but Jacob never cared for her after that terrible awakening to find her face on the pillow when, after seven years' toil, he wanted the expected Rachel.

So Fra. P., after five years barking up the wrong tree, had lost interest in trees altogether as far as climbing them was concerned. He might indulge in a little human pride: "See, Jack, that's the branch I cut my name on when I was a boy"; but even had he seen in the forest the Tree of Life itself with the golden fruit of Eternity in its branches, he would have done no more than lift his gun and shoot the pigeon that flitted through its foliage.

Of this " withdrawal from the vision " the proof is not merely deducible from the absence of all occult documents in his dossier, and from the full occupation of his life in external and mundane duties and pleasures, but is made irrefragible and emphatic by the positive evidence of his writings. Of these we have several examples. Two are dramatisations of Greek mythology, a subject offering every opportunity to the occultist. Both are markedly free from any such allusions. We have also a slim booklet, 'Rosa Mundi,' in which the joys of pure human love are pictured without the faintest tinge of mystic emotion. Further, we have a play, 'The God Eater,' in which the Origin of Religion, as conceived by Spencer or Frazer, is dramatically shown forth; and lastly we have a satire, 'Why Jesus Wept,' hard, cynical, and brutal in its estimate of society, but careless of any remedy for its ills.

It is as if the whole past of the man with all its aspiration and attainment was blotted out. He saw life (for the first time, perhaps) with commonplace human eyes. Cynicism he could understand, romance he could understand; all beyond was dark. Happiness was the bedfellow of contempt.

We learn that, late in 1903, he was proposing to visit China on a sporting expedition, when a certain very commonplace communication made to him by his wife caused him to postpone it. " Let's go and kill something for a month or two," said he, " and if you're right, we'll get back to nurses and doctors."

So we find them in Hambantota, the south-eastern province

of Ceylon, occupied solely with buffalo, elephant, leopard, sambhur, and the hundred other objects of the chase.

We here insert extracts from the diary, indeed a meagre production—after what we have seen of his previous record in Ceylon.

Whole weeks pass without a word; the great man was playing bridge, poker, or golf!

The entry of February 19th reads as if it were going to be interesting, but it is followed by that of February 20th. It is however certain that about the 14th of March he took possession of a flat in Cairo—in the Season!

Can bathos go further?

So that the entry of March 16th is dated from Cairo.

(Our notes are given in round brackets.)

Frater P.'s Diary

(This diary is extremely incomplete and fragmentary. Many entries, too, are evidently irrelevant or "blinds." We omit much of the latter two types.)

"This eventful year 1903 finds me at a nameless camp in the jungle of a Southern Province of Ceylon; my thoughts, otherwise divided between Yoga and sport, are diverted by the fact of a wife . . ."

(This reference to Yoga is the subconscious Magical Will of the Vowed Initiate. He was not doing anything; but, on questioning himself, as was his custom at certain seasons, he felt obliged to affirm his Aspiration.)

Jan. 1 . . . (Much blotted out) . . . missed deer and hare. So annoyed. Yet the omen is that the year is well for works of Love and Union; ill for those of Hate. Be mine of Love! (Note that he does not add "and Union.")[1]

Jan. 28 Embark for Suez.

Feb. 7 Suez.

Feb. 8 Landed at Port Said.

Feb. 9 To Cairo.

Feb. 11 Saw b.f.g.
b.f.b.
(This entry is quite unintelligible to us.)

Feb. 19 To Helwan as Oriental Despot.
(Apparently P. had assumed some disguise, probably with the intention of trying to study Islam from within as he had done with Hinduism.)

Feb. 20 Began golf.

March 16 Began INV. (invocation) IAO[2]

March 17 ⲑⲱⲟⲩⲧ appeared.[3]

March 18 Told to INV. (invoke) Ϧⲱⲱⲣⲓ[4] as ☉[5] by new way.

March 19 Did this badly at noon 30.

March 20 At 10 p.m. did well—Equinox of Gods—Nov—(? new) C.R.C. (Christian Rosy Cross, we conjecture.) Hoori now Hpnt (obviously "Hierophant").

March 21 in . I.A.M. (? one o'clock)

March 22 X.P.B.
(May this and the entry March 24, refer to the

[1] As a devotee of Yoga, "Union," would have done.
[2] Given in Liber Samekh: see "Magick."
[3] Thoth, the Egyptian God of Wisdom and Magick.
[4] Horus.
[5] The Sun.

brother of the A.·.A.·. who found him ?)
E.P.D. in 84 m.
(Unintelligible to us ; probably a blind.)

March 23 Y.K. done. (?His work on the Yi King.)[1]
March 24 Met اجيبحا again.
March 25 823 Thus
461 „ „=p f l y 2 b z
218
(Blot) wch trouble with ds.
(Blot) P.B. (All unintelligible ; possibly a blind.)
April 6 Go off again to H, taking A's p.
(This is probably a blind.)

Before we go further into the history of this period we must premise as follows.

Fra. P. never made a thorough record of this period. He seems to have wavered between absolute scepticism in the bad sense, a dislike of the revelation, on the one hand, and real enthusiasm on the other. And the first of these moods would induce him to do things to spoil the effect of the latter. Hence the " blinds " and stupid meaningless cyphers which deface the diary.

And, as if the Gods themselves wished to darken the Pylon, we find later, when P.'s proud will had been broken, and he wished to make straight the way of the historian, his memory (one of the finest memories in the world) was utterly incompetent to make everything certain.

However, nothing of which he was not certain will be entered in this place.

We have one quite unspoiled and authoritative document,

[1] More probably a blind.

" The Book of Results," written in one of the small Japanese vellum note-books which he used to carry. Unfortunately, it seems to have been abandoned after five days. What happened between March 23rd and April 8th ?

THE BOOK OF RESULTS.

March 16th Die ☿[1] I invoke IAO.

(Fra. P. tells us that this was done by the ritual of the " Bornless One," identical with the " Preliminary Invocation "[2] in the " Goetia," merely to amuse his wife by showing her the sylphs. She refused or was unable to see any sylphs, but became " inspired," and kept on saying : " They're waiting for you ! ")

(Note. The maiden name of his wife was Rose Edith Kelly. He called her Ouarda, the Arabic for " Rose." She is hereafter signified by " Ouarda the Seer " or "W." for short. Ed.)

W. says " they " are " waiting for me."

17. ♃[3] It is " all about the child." Also " all Osiris." (Note the cynic and sceptic tone of this entry. How different it appears in the light of Liber 418 !) Thoth, invoked with great success, indwells us. (Yes ; but what happened ? Fra.P. has no sort of idea.)

18. ♀[4] Revealed that the waiter was Horus, whom I had offended and ought to invoke. The ritual revealed in skeleton. Promise of success ♄[5] or ☉[6] and of Samadhi.

(Is this " waiter " another sneer ? We are uncertain.)

[1] I.e. Wednesday. [2] See " Magick " Appendix Liber CXX.
[3] Thursday. [4] Friday. [5] Saturday. [6] Sunday.

> The revealing of the ritual (by W. the seer) consisted chiefly in a prohibition of all formulae hitherto used, as will be seen from the text printed below.

It was probably on this day that P. cross-examined W. about Horus. Only the striking character of her identification of the God, surely, would have made him trouble to obey her. He remembers that he only agreed to obey her in order to show her how silly she was, and he taunted her that "nothing could happen if you broke all the rules."

Here therefore we insert a short note by Fra. P. how W. knew R.H.K. (Ra Hoor Khuit)

1. Force and Fire (I asked her to describe his moral qualities.)
2. Deep blue light. (I asked her to describe the conditions caused by him. This light is quite unmistakable and unique; but of course her words, though a fair description of it, might equally apply to some other.)
3. Horus. (I asked her to pick out his name from a list of ten dashed off at haphazard.)
4. Recognized his figure when shown. (This refers to the striking scene in the Boulak Museum, which will be dealt with in detail.)
5. Knew my past relations with the God. (This means, I think, that she knew I had taken his place in temple,[1] etc., and that I had never once invoked him.)
6. Knew his enemy. (I asked, "Who is his enemy?" Reply, "Forces of the waters—of the Nile." W. knew no Egyptology—or anything else.)
7. Knew his lineal figure and its colour. (A 1/84 chance.)

[1] See Equinox Vol. I, No. II, the Neophyte Ritual of the G.·.D.·.

8. Knew his place in temple. (A $\frac{1}{4}$ chance, at the least.)
9. Knew his weapon (from a list of 6.)
10. Knew his planetary nature (from a list of 7 planets.)
11. Knew his number (from a list of 10 units.)
12. Picked him out of (a) Five / (b) Three } indifferent, i.e. arbitrary symbols. (This means that I settled in my own mind that say D of A,B,C,D, and E should represent him, and that she then said D.)

We cannot too strongly insist on the extraordinary character of this identification.

We had made no pretension to clairvoyance; nor had P. ever tried to train her.

P. had great experience with clairvoyants, and it was always a point of honour with him to bowl them out. And here was a novice, a woman who should never have been allowed outside a ballroom, speaking with the authority of God, and proving it by unhesitating correctness.

One slip, and Fra. P. would have sent her to the devil. And that slip was not made. Calculate the odds! We cannot find a mathematical expression for tests 1,2,3,4,5, or 6, but the other 7 tests give us

$$\frac{1}{10} \times \frac{1}{84} \times \frac{1}{4} \times \frac{1}{6} \times \frac{1}{7} \times \frac{1}{10} \times \frac{1}{15} = \frac{1}{21,168,000}$$

Twenty-one millions to one against her getting through half the ordeal!

Even if we suppose what is absurd, that she knew the correspondences of the Qabalah as well as Fra. P., and had knowledge of his own secret relations with the Unseen, we must strain telepathy to explain test 12.

(Note. We may add, too, that Fra. P. thinks, but is not quite certain, that he also tested her with the Hebrew Alphabet and the Tarot trumps, in which case the long odds must be still further multiplied by 484, bringing them over the billion mark!)

But we know that she was perfectly ignorant of the subtle correspondences, which were only existing at that time in Fra. P.'s own brain.

And even if it were so, how are we to explain what followed —the discovery of the Stélé of Revealing?

To apply test 4, Fra.P. took her to the museum at Boulak, which they had not previously visited. She passed by (as P. noted with silent glee) several images of Horus. They went upstairs. A glass case stood in the distance, too far off for its contents to be recognized. But W. recognized it! "There," she cried, "There he is!"

Fra. P. advanced to the case. There was the image of Horus in the form of Ra Hoor Khuit painted upon a wooden stélé of the 26th dynasty—and the exhibit bore the number 666![1]

(And after that it was five years before Fra.P. was forced to obedience!)

This incident must have occurred before the 23rd of March, as the entry on that date refers to Ankh-f-n-khonsu.

Here is P.'s description of the stélé.

"In the museum at Cairo, No. 666 is the stélé of the Priest Ankh-f-n-khonsu.

Horus has a red Disk and green Uraeus.

[1] 666 had been taken by Fra. P. as the number of His own Name (The Beast) long years before, in His childhood. There could be no physical causal connection here; and coincidence, sufficient to explain this one isolated fact, becomes inadequate in view of the other evidence.

His face is green, his skin indigo.
His necklace, anklets, and bracelets are gold.
His nemyss nearly black from blue.
His tunic is the Leopard's skin, and his apron green and gold.
Green is the wand of double Power ; his r.h. is empty.
His throne is indigo the gnomon, red the square.
The light is gamboge.
Above him are the Winged Globe and the bent figure of the heavenly Isis, her hands and feet touching earth.

(We print the most recent translation of the Stélé, by Messrs. Alan Gardiner, Litt.D., and Battiscombe Gunn. It differs slightly from that used by Fra. P., which was due to the assistant-curator of the Museum at Boulak.)

STELE OF ANKH-F-NA-KHONSU.

Obverse.

Topmost Register (under Winged Disk)
Behdet (? Hadit ?), the Great God, the Lord of Heaven.
Middle Register. Two vertical lines to left :—
Ra-Harakhti, Master of the Gods.
Five vertical lines to right :—
Osiris, the Priest of Montu, Lord of Thebes, Opener of the doors of Nut in Karnak, Ankh-f-n-Khonsu, the Justified.
Below Altar :—
Oxen, Geese, Wine (?), Bread.
Behind the god is the hieroglyph of Amenti.
Lowest Register.
(1) Saith Osiris, the Priest of Montu, Lord of Thebes, the opener of the Doors of Nut in Karnak, Ankh-f-n-Khonsu, (2)

the Justified :—" Hail, Thou whose praise is high (the highly praised), thou great-willed. O Soul (ba) very awful (lit. mighty, of awe) that giveth the terror of him (3) among the Gods, shining in glory upon his great throne, making ways for the Soul (ba) for the Spirit (yekh) and for the Shadow (khabt) : I am prepared and I shine forth as one that is prepared. (4) I have made way to the place in which are Ra, Tom, Khepri and Hathor." Osiris, the Priest of Montu, Lord of Thebes (5) Ankh-f-na-Khonsu, the Justified ; son of MNB SNMT[1]; born of the Sistrum-bearer of Amon, the Lady Atne-sher.

Reverse.

Eleven lines of writing.

(1) Saith Osiris, the Priest of Montu, Lord of Thebes, Ankh-f-(2)na-Khonsu, the Justified :—" My heart from my mother, my heart (different word, apparently synonymous, but probably not so at all) of my existence (3) upon earth, stand not forth against me as witness, drive me not back (4) among the Sovereign Judges (quite an arbitrary conventional translation of the original word), neither incline against me in the presence of the Great God, the Lord of the West (Osiris of course) : (5) Now that I am united with Earth in the Great West, and endure no longer upon Earth.

(6). Saith Osiris, he who is in Thebes, Ankh-f-na-Khonsu, the Justified : " O Only (7) One, shining like (or in) the Moon; Osiris Ankh-f-(8)na-Khonsu has come forth upon high among these thy multitudes. (9) He that gathereth together those that are in the Light, the Underworld (duat) is (also) (10)

([1]The father's name. The method of spelling shows that he was a foreigner. There is no clue to the vocalisation).

F

opened to him; lo Osiris Ankh-f-na-Khonsu, cometh forth (11) by day to do all that he wisheth upon earth among the living."

There is one other object to complete the secret of Wisdom —(P. notes "perhaps a Thoth") or it is in the hieroglyphs. (This last paragraph is, we suppose, dictated by W.)

We now return to the "Book of Results."

19 The ritual written out and the invocation done— little success.

20 Revealed (We cannot make out if this revelation comes from W. or is a result of the ritual. But almost certainly the former, as it precedes the "Great Success" entry) that the Equinox of the Gods is come, Horus taking the Throne of the East and all rituals, etc., being abrogated.

(To explain this[1] we append to this chapter the G.D. ritual of the Equinox, which was celebrated in the spring and autumn within 48 hours of the actual dates of Sol entering Aries and Libra.)

20 (contd.) Great success in midnight invocation.

(The other diary says 10 P.M. "Midnight" is perhaps a loose phrase, or perhaps marks the climax of the ritual.)

I am to formulate a new link of an Order with the Solar Force.

(It is not clear what happened in this invocation; but it is evident from another note of certainly later date, that "great success" does not mean "Samadhi." For P. writes: "I

[1] The analogy is between the "new formula" given by the "Word" every six months in the Order, and that given every couple of thousand years (more or less) by the Word of a Magus to the whole or part of Mankind.

make it an absolute condition that I should attain Samadhi in the god's own interest." His memory concurs in this. It was the Samadhi attained in October, 1906, that set him again in the path of obedience to this revelation.

But that "great success" means something very important is clear enough. The sneering sceptic of the 17th of March must have had a shock before he wrote those words.)

21. ☾.☉ enters ♈.[1]

22. ♂[2] The day of rest, on which nothing whatever of magic is to be done at all. ☿[3] is to be the great day of invocation.

(This note is due to W.'s prompting or to his own rationalizing imagination.)

23. The Secret of Wisdom.

(We omit the record of a long and futile Tarot divination.)

At this point we may insert the Ritual which was so successful on the 20th.

INVOCATION OF HORUS
ACCORDING TO THE DIVINE VISION OF W., THE SEER.

To be performed before a window open to the E. or N. without incense. The room to be filled with jewels, but only diamonds to be worn. A sword, unconsecrated, 44 pearl beads to be told. Stand. Bright daylight at 12.30 noon. Lock doors. White robes. Bare feet. Be very loud. Saturday. Use the Sign of Apophis and Typhon.

[1] "Monday. The Sun enters Aries." i.e. Spring begins. [2] Tuesday.
[3] Wednesday.

The above is W.'s answer to various questions posed by P.

Preliminary. Banish. L.B.R. Pentagram. L.B.R. Hexagram. Flaming sword. Abrahadabra, Invoke. As before.

(These are P.'s ideas for the ritual. W. replied, "Omit.")

The MS. of this Ritual bears many internal marks of having been written at white heat and left unrevised, save perhaps for one glance. There are mistakes in grammar and spelling unique in all MSS. of Fra. P.; the use of capitals is irregular, and the punctuation almost wanting.)

CONFESSION.

Unprepared and uninvoking Thee, I, ΟΥ ΜΗ, Fra R.R. et A.C., am here in Thy Presence—for Thou art Everywhere, O Lord Horus!—to confess humbly before Thee my neglect and scorn of Thee.

How shall I humble myself enough before Thee? Thou art the mighty and unconquered Lord of the Universe: I am a spark of Thine unutterable Radiance.

How should I approach Thee? but Thou art Everywhere.

But Thou hast graciously deigned to call me unto Thee, to this Exorcism of Art, that I may be Thy Servant, Thine Adept, O Bright One, O Sun of Glory! Thou hast called me—should I not then hasten to Thy Presence?

With unwashen hands therefore I come unto Thee, and I lament my wandering from Thee—but Thou knowest!

Yea, I have done evil!

If one (doubtless a reference to S.R.M.D. who was much obsessed by Mars, P. saw Horus at first as Geburah; later as an aspect of Tiphereth, including Chesed and Geburah—the red Triangle inverted—an aspect opposite to Osiris.) blasphemed Thee, why should I therefore forsake Thee? But Thou art the Avenger; all is with Thee.

I bow my neck before Thee; and as once Thy sword was upon it (see G∴ D∴ Ceremony of Neophyte, the Obligation), so am I in Thy hands. Strike if Thou wilt: spare if Thou wilt: but accept me as I am.

My trust is in Thee: shall I be confounded? This Ritual of Art; this Forty and Fourfold Invocation; this Sacrifice of Blood—(Merely, we suppose, that 44=DM, blood. Possibly a bowl of blood was used. P. thinks it was in some of the workings at this time, but is not sure if it was this one.)—these I do not comprehend.

It is enough if I obey Thy decree; did Thy fiat go forth for my eternal misery, were it not my joy to execute Thy Sentence on myself?

For why? For that All is in Thee and of Thee; it is enough if I burn up in the intolerable glory of Thy presence.

Enough! I turn toward Thy Promise.

Doubtful are the Words: Dark are the Ways: but in Thy Words and Ways is Light. Thus then now as ever, I enter the Path of Darkness, if haply so I may attain the Light.

Hail!

α I א

Strike, strike the master chord!
Draw, draw the Flaming Sword!
Crowned Child and Conquering Lord,
Horus, avenger!

1. O Thou of the Head of the Hawk! Thee, Thee, I invoke!

(At every "Thee I invoke," throughout whole ritual, give the sign of Apophis.)

A. Thou only-begotten-child of Osiris Thy Father, and Isis Thy Mother. He that was slain; She that bore Thee in Her womb flying from the Terror of the Water. Thee, Thee I invoke!

2. O Thou whose Apron is of flashing white, whiter than the Forehead of the Morning! Thee, Thee, I invoke!

B. O Thou who hast formulated Thy Father and made fertile Thy Mother! Thee, Thee, I invoke!

3. O Thou whose garment is of golden glory with the azure bars of sky! Thee, Thee, I invoke!

C. Thou, who didst avenge the Horror of Death; Thou the slayer of Typhon! Thou who didst lift Thine arms, and the Dragons of Death were as dust; Thou who didst raise Thine Head, and the Crocodile of Nile was abased before Thee! Thee, Thee, I invoke!

4. O Thou whose Nemyss hideth the Universe with night, the impermeable Blue! Thee, Thee, I invoke!

D. Thou who travellest in the Boat of Ra, abiding at the Helm of the Aftet boat and of the Sektet boat! Thee, Thee, I invoke!

5. Thou who bearest the Wand of Double Power! Thee, Thee, I invoke!

E. Thou about whose presence is shed the darkness of Blue Light, the unfathomable glory of the outmost Ether, the untravelled, the unthinkable immensity of

Space. Thou who concentrest all the Thirty Ethers in one darkling sphere of Fire! Thee, Thee, I invoke!

6. O Thou who bearest the Rose and Cross of Life and Light! Thee, Thee, I invoke!

The Voice of the Five.
The Voice of the Six.
Eleven are the Voices.
Abrahadabra!

β II ב

Strike, strike the master chord!
Draw, draw the Flaming Sword!
Crowned Child and Conquering Lord,
Horus, Avenger!

1. By thy name of Ra, I invoke Thee, Hawk of the Sun, the glorious one!
2. By thy name Harmachis, youth of the Brilliant Morning, I invoke Thee!
3. By thy name Mau, I invoke Thee, Lion of the Midday Sun!
4. By thy name Tum, Hawk of the Even, crimson splendour of the Sunset, I invoke Thee!
5. By thy name Khep-Ra I invoke Thee, O Beetle of the hidden Mastery of Midnight!

A. By thy name Heru-pa-Kraat, Lord of Silence, Beautiful Child that standest on the Dragons of the Deep, I invoke Thee!

B. By thy name Apollo, I invoke Thee, O man of Strength and splendour, O poet, O father!

C. By thy name of Phoebus, that drivest thy chariot through the Heaven of Zeus, I invoke Thee!

D. By thy name of Odin I invoke Thee, O warrior of the North, O Renown of the Sagas!

E. By thy name of Jeheshua, O child of the Flaming Star, I invoke Thee!

F. By Thine own, Thy secret name Hoori, Thee I invoke!

The Names are Five.
The Names are Six.
Eleven are the Names!
Abrahadabra!

Behold! I stand in the midst. Mine is the symbol of Osiris; to Thee are mine eyes ever turned. Unto the splendour of Geburah, the Magnificence of Chesed, the mystery of Daath, thither I lift up mine eyes. This have I sought, and I have sought the Unity: hear Thou me!

γ III ג

1. Mine is the Head of the Man, and my insight is keen as the Hawk's. By my head I invoke Thee!

A. I am the only-begotten child of my Father and Mother. By my body I invoke Thee!

2. About me shine the Diamonds of Radiance white and pure. By their brightness I invoke Thee!

B. Mine is the Red Triangle Reversed, the Sign given of none, save it be of Thee, O Lord! (This sign had been previously communicated by W. It was entirely new to P.) By the Lamen I invoke Thee!

3. Mine is the garment of white sewn with gold, the flashing abbai that I wear. By my robe I invoke Thee!

C. Mine is the sign of Apophis and Typhon! By the sign I invoke Thee!

4. Mine is the turban of white and gold, and mine the blue vigour of the intimate air! By my crown I invoke Thee!

D. My fingers travel on the Beads of Pearl; so run I after Thee in thy car of glory. By my fingers I invoke Thee! (On Saturday the string of pearls broke: so I changed the invocation to "My mystic sigils travel in the Bark of the Akasa, etc. By the spells I invoke Thee!—P.)

5. I bear the Wand of Double Power in the Voice of the Master—Abrahadabra! By the word I invoke Thee!

E. Mine are the dark-blue waves of music in the song that I made of old to invoke Thee—

> Strike, strike the master chord!
> Draw, draw the Flaming Sword!
> Crowned Child and Conquering Lord,
>   Horus, avenger!

By the Song I invoke Thee!

6. In my hand is thy Sword of Revenge; let it strike at Thy Bidding! By the Sword I invoke Thee!

> The Voice of the Five.
> The Voice of the Six.
> Eleven are the Voices.
>   Abrahadabra!

δ IV ד

(This section merely repeats section I in the first person. Thus it begins: 1. "Mine is the Head of the Hawk! Abrahadabra!" and ends: 6. "I bear the Rose and Cross of Life and Light! Abrahadabra!" giving the Sign at each Abrahadabra. Remaining in the Sign, the invocation concludes:)

> Therefore I say unto thee: Come Thou forth and dwell in me; so that every my Spirit, whether of the Firmament, or of the Ether, or of the Earth or under the Earth; on dry land or in the Water, or Whirling Air or of Rushing Fire; and every spell and scourge of God the Vast One may be THOU. Abrahadabra!

The Adoration—impromptu.

Close by banishing. (I think this was omitted at W.'s order.—P.)

. . . . . .

During the period March 23rd—April 8th, whatever else may have happened, it is at least certain that work was continued to some extent, that the inscriptions of the stélé were translated for Fra.P., and that he paraphrased the latter in verse. For we find him using, or prepared to use, the same in the text of Liber Legis.

Perhaps then, perhaps later, he made out the "name-coincidences of the Qabalah," to which we must now direct the reader's attention.

The MS. is a mere fragmentary sketch.

Ch = 8 = ChITh = 418 = Abrahadabra = RA-HVVR (Ra-Hoor).

Also 8 is the great symbol I adore.

(This may be because of its likeness to ∞ or because of its [old G.·.D.·.] attributions to Daath, P. being then a rationalist; or for some other reason.)

So is O.

O=A in the Book of Thoth (The Tarot).

A=111 with all its great meanings, ⊙=6.

Now 666=My name, the number of the stélé, the number of The Beast (See Apocalypse), the number of the Man.

The Beast AChIHA=666 in full. (The usual spelling is ChIVA.)

(A=111, Ch=418, I=20, H=6, A=111.)

HRV-RA-HA. 211+201+6=418.

(This name occurs only in L. Legis, and is a test of that book rather than of the stélé.)

ANKH-P-N-KHONShU-T=666.

(We trust the addition of the termination T will be found justified.)

{Bes-n-maut, B I Sh N A - M A V T } =888.
{Ta-Nich, Th A - N I Ch } =Ch x A.

Nuteru NVThIRV=666.

Montu MVNTV=111.

Aiwass AIVAS=78, the influence or messenger, or the Book T. (P.S. Note this error! Ed.)

Ta-Nich TA-NICh=78. Alternatively, Sh for Ch gives 370, O Sh, Creation.

So much we extract from volumes filled with minute calculations, of which the bulk is no longer intelligible even to Fra. P.

His memory, however, assures us that the coincidences were

much more numerous and striking than those we have been able to reproduce here; but his attitude is, we understand, that after all "It's all in Liber Legis. 'Success is thy proof: argue not; convert not; talk not overmuch!'" And indeed in the Commentary to that Book will be found sufficient for the most wary of inquirers.

Now who, it may be asked, was Aiwass? It is the name given by W. to P. as that of her informant. Also it is the name given as that of the revealer of Liber Legis. But whether Aiwass is a spiritual being, or a man known to Fra. P., is a matter of the merest conjecture. His number is 78[1], that of Mezla, the Channel through which Macroprosopus reveals Himself to, or showers His influence upon, Microposopus.[2] So we find Fra. P. speaking of him at one time as of another, but more advanced man; at another time as if it were the name of his own superior in the Spiritual Hierarchy. And to all questions Fra. P. finds a reply, either pointing out "the subtle metaphysical distinction between curiosity and hard work," or indicating that among the Brethren "names are only lies," or in some other way defeating the very plain purpose of the historian.

The same remark applies to all queries with regard to V.V.V.V.V.;[3] with this addition, that in this case he condescends to argue and to instruct. "If I tell you," he once said to the present writer,[4] "that V.V.V.V.V. is a Mr. Smith and lives at Clapham, you will at once go round and tell every-

[1] But see the miraculous events connected with "The Revival of Magick" described in Magick pp. 257–260, where he is shewn as 93.

[2] I.e. the messenger of God to Man.

[3] The motto of Fra. P. as a Magister Templi 8°=3▫; He used it in His office of giving out the "Official Books of A.'.A.'." to the world in the Equinox.

[4] J. F. C. Fuller.

body that V.V.V.V.V. is a Mr. Smith of Clapham, which is not true. V.V.V.V.V. is the Light of the World itself, the sole Mediator between God and Man; and in your present frame of mind (that of a poopstick) you cannot see that the two statements may be identical for the Brothers of the A.·.A.·.! Did not your great-grandfather argue that no good thing could come out of Nazareth? 'Is not this the carpenter's son? is not his mother called Mary? and his brethren, James and Joses, and Simon, and Judas? And his sisters, are they not all with us? Whence then hath this man all these things? And they were offended in him.'"

Similarly with regard to the writing of Liber Legis, Fr. P. will only say that it is in no way "automatic writing," that he heard clearly and distinctly the human articulate accents of a man. Once, on page 6, he is told to edit a sentence; and once, on page 19, W. supplies a sentence which he had failed to hear.

To this writing we now turn.

It must have been on the 7th of April that W. commanded P. (now somewhat cowed) to enter the "temple" exactly at 12 o'clock noon on three successive days, and to write down what he should hear, rising exactly at 1 o'clock.

This he did. Immediately on his taking his seat the Voice began its Utterance, and ended exactly at the expiration of the hour.

These are the three chapters of Liber Legis, and we have nothing to add.

The full title of the book is, as P. first chose to name it,

LIBER L vel LEGIS
sub figura CCXX
as delivered by LXXVIII to DCLXVI

and it is the First and Greatest of those Class A publications of A.·.A.·. of which is not to be altered so much as the style of a letter.

This was the original title devised by 666 to appear in the 1909 publication. The "Key of it all" and the true spelling of Aiwass had not then been discovered.

FESTIVAL OF THE EQUINOX.

(Temple arranged as for $0° = 0^{□}$.)

Ht. (knocks) Fratres and Sorores of all grades of the Golden Dawn in the Outer, let us celebrate the Festival of the (Vernal) Autumnal Equinox!
All rise.

Ht. Frater Kerux, proclaim the fact, and announce the abrogation of the present Pass Word.

K. (Going to Ht.'s right, saluting, and facing West). In the Name of the Lord of the Universe, and by command of the V.H.Ht., I proclaim the {Vernal / Autumnal} Equinox, and declare that the Pass Word . . . . . . is abrogated.

Ht. Let us, according to ancient custom, consecrate the return of the {Vernal / Autumnal} Equinox.

Light.

Hs. Darkness.

Ht. East.

Hs. West.

Ht. Air.

Hs. Water.

Hg. (knocks) I am the Reconciler between them.

All give signs.

D. Heat.

S. Cold.

D. South.

S. North.

D. Fire.

S. Earth.

Hg. (knocks) I am the Reconciler between them.

All give signs.

Ht. (knocks) One Creator.

D. One Preserver.

Hs. (knocks) One Destroyer.

S. One Redeemer.

Hg. (knocks) One Reconciler between them.

All give signs.

Each retiring officer in turn, beginning with Ht. quits his post by the left hand and goes to the foot of Throne. He there disrobes, placing robe and lamen at foot of Throne or Dais. He then proceeds with the Sun's course to the Altar, and lays thereon his special insignia, viz: Ht., Sceptre: Hs., Sword: Hg., Sceptre: K., Lamp and Wand: S., Cup: D., Censer: repeating out-going Password as he does so.

Ht. taking from the Altar the Rose, returns with the Sun to his post :

Hs. takes Cup of Wine :

Hf. waits for the Kerux and takes his Red Lamp from him.

K. takes nothing.

S. takes platter of salt.

D. takes emblem of Elemental Fire.

Returning each to his place.

The remaining members form a column in the North and, led by Kerux, proceed to the East ; when all are in column along East side each turns to the left and faces Hierophant.

Ht. Let us adore the Lord of the Universe.

Holy art Thou, Lord of the Air, who has created the Firmament. (Making with the Rose the sign of the Cross in the Air towards the East.)

All give signs. Procession moves on to the South, halts, and all face South.

D. (facing South) Let us adore the Lord of the Universe. Holy art Thou, Lord of the Fire, wherein Thou hast shown forth the Throne of Thy Glory. (Making with the Fire the sign of the Cross towards the South.)

All give signs. Procession moves on to the West, halts, and faces West.

Hs. (facing West) Let us adore the Lord of the Universe. Holy art Thou, Lord of the Waters, whereon Thy Spirit moved at the beginning. (Making with the Cup the sign of the Cross in the Air before him.)

All give signs. Procession passes on to the North. All halt and face North.

S. (facing North) Let us adore the Lord of the Universe. Holy art Thou, Lord of the Earth, which Thou hast made Thy footstool. (Making with the platter of Salt the sign of the Cross toward the North.)

All give signs. All resume their places and face the usual way.

Hg. Let us adore the Lord of the Universe.
Holy art Thou, Who art in all things, in Whom are all things;
If I climb up into Heaven, Thou art there;
If I go down into Hell, Thou art there also;
If I take the Wings of the Morning and remain in the uttermost parts of the Sea, even there shall Thy hand lead me and Thy right hand shall hold me.
If I say "Peradventure the Darkness shall cover me," even the Night shall be Light unto Thee.
Thine is the Air with its Movement.
Thine is the Fire with its flashing Flame.
Thine is the Water with its Flux and Reflux.
Thine is the Earth with its Eternal Stability.
(Makes the sign of the Cross with Red Lamp.)

All give signs. Ht. goes to Altar and deposits Rose. Imperator meanwhile assumes the Throne.

Ht. returns to a seat on the immediate left as Past Hierophant. Each old Officer now proceeds in turn to Altar and places upon it the ensign he had taken therefrom, returning to places of their grade, not their Thrones, with nothing in their hands: they sit as common members, leaving all offices vacant.

Imperator. By the Power and Authority in me vested, I

confer upon you the new Pass Word. It is . . . . . .

The Officers of this Temple for the ensuing half-year are as follows :—

(Reads list of New Officers.)

New Officers come up in turn and are robed by the Imperator. Each new Officer in turn passes to the Altar and takes his insignia therefrom, repeating aloud :

By the Pass Word . . . . . . I claim my . . . . . .

S., after claiming his Cup, purifies the Hall and the Members by Water, without a word spoken by the Ht. unless he fails in this duty.

D., after claiming his Censer, consecrates the Hall and the Members by Fire, without unnecessary word from Ht.

THE MYSTIC CIRCUMAMBULATION.

This should take place in Silence, but if the Members be unprovided with Rituals, the Ht. may order it as follows : All form in North, K., Hg., Members, Hs., S., D.

Each Member as he passes the Throne repeats the Pass Word aloud.

Ht. Let us invoke the Lord of the Universe.

Lord of the Universe, Blessed be Thy Name unto the Eternal Ages.

Look with favour upon this Order, and grant that its members may at length attain to the true Summum Bonum, the Stone of the Wise, the Perfect Wisdom and the Eternal Light.

To the Glory of Thine Ineffable Name. AMEN.

All salute.

Ht. Frater Kerux, in the Name of the Lord of the Universe, I command you to declare that the {Vernal / Autumnal} Equinox has returned, and that . . . . . . is the Pass Word for the next six months.

K. In the Name of the Lord of the Universe and by command of the V.H.Ht. I declare that the Sun has entered {Aries / Libra}, the Sign of the {Vernal / Autumnal} Equinox, and that the Pass Word for the ensuing half-year will be . . . . . .

Ht.	Khabs.	Pax.	In.
Hs.	Am.	Konx.	Extension.
Hg.	Pekht.	Om.	Light.

CHAPTER VII.

Remarks on the method of receiving Liber Legis, on the Conditions prevailing at the time of the writing, and on certain technical difficulties connected with the Literary form of the Book.[1]

I

Certain very serious questions have arisen with regard to the method by which this Book was obtained. I do not refer to those doubts—real or pretended—which hostility engenders, for all such are dispelled by study of the text; no forger could have prepared so complex a set of numerical and literal puzzles as to leave himself (a) devoted to the solution for years after, (b) baffled by a simplicity which when disclosed leaves one gasping at its profundity, (c) enlightened only by progressive initiation, or by "accidental" events apparently disconnected with the Book, which occurred long after its publication, (d) hostile, bewildered, and careless even in the face of independent testimony as to the power and clarity of the Book, and of the fact that by Its light other men have attained the loftiest summits of initiation in a tithe of the time which history and experience would lead one to expect, and (e) angrily unwilling to proceed with that part of the Work

[1] This paper was written, independently of any idea of its present place in this Book, by The Beast 666 Himself, in the Abbey of Thelema in Cefalù, Sicily. No further apology is offered for any repetitions of statements made in previous chapters.

appointed for him which is detailed in Chapter III, even when the course of events on the planet, war, revolution, and the collapse of the social and religious systems of civilization, proved plainly to him that whether he liked it or no, Ra Hoor Khuit was indeed Lord of the Aeon, the Crowned and Conquering Child whose innocence meant no more than inhuman cruelty and wantonly senseless destructiveness as he avenged Isis our mother the Earth and the Heaven for the murder and mutilation of Osiris, Man, her son. The War of 1914-18 and its sequels have proved even to the dullest statesmen, beyond wit of even the most subtly sophistical theologians to gloze, that death is not an unmixed benefit either to the individual or the community : that force and fire of leaping manhood are more useful to a nation than cringing respectability and emasculate servility ; that genius goes with courage, and the sense of shame and guilt with " Defeatism."

For these reasons and many more I am certain, I the Beast, whose number is Six Hundred and Sixty and Six, that this Third Chapter of the Book of the Law is nothing less than the authentic Word, the Word of the Aeon, the Truth about Nature at this time and on this planet. I wrote it, hating it and sneering at it, secretly glad that I could use it to revolt against this Task most terrible that the Gods have thrust remorselessly upon my shoulders, their Cross of burning steel that I must carry even to my Calvary, the place of a skull, there to be eased of its weight only that I be crucified thereon. But, being lifted up, I will draw the whole world unto me ; and men shall worship me the Beast, Six Hundred and Threescore and Six, celebrating to Me their Midnight Mass every time soever when they do that they will, and on Mine altar slaying to Me that victim I most relish, their Selves; when Love designs and Will executes the Rite whereby (an they know it or know not) their God in man is offered to me The Beast, their God, the Rite whose virtue, making their God of their throned Beast, leaves nothing, howso bestial, undivine.

On such lines my own "conversion" to my own "religion" may yet take place, though as I write these words all but twelve weeks of Sixteen years are well nigh past.[1]

II

This long digression is but to explain that I, myself, who issue Liber Legis, am no fanatic partisan. I will obey my orders (III, 42) "Argue not, convert not;" even though I shirk some others. I shall not deign to answer sceptical enquiries as to the origin of the Book. "Success is your proof." I, of all men on this Earth reputed mightiest in Magick, by mine enemies more than by my friends, have striven to lose this Book, to forget it, defy it, criticise it, escape it, these nigh sixteen years; and It holds me to the course It sets, even as the Mountain of Lodestone holds the ship, or Helios by invisible bonds controls his planets; yea, or as BABALON grips between her thighs the Great Wild Beast she straddles!

So much for the sceptics; put your heads in the Lion's mouth; so may you come to certainty, whether I be stuffed with straw!

But, in the text of the Book itself, are thorns for the flesh of the most ardent swain as he buries his face in the roses; some

[1] Written in 1920, e. v.

of the ivy that clings about the Thyrse of this Dionysus is Poison Ivy. The question arises, especially on examining the original manuscript in My handwriting: "Who wrote these words?"

Of course I wrote them, ink on paper, in the material sense; but they are not My words, unless Aiwaz be taken to be no more than my subconscious self, or some part of it: in that case, my conscious self being ignorant of the Truth in the Book and hostile to most of the ethics and philosophy of the Book, Aiwaz is a severely suppressed part of me.[1] If so, the theorist must suggest a reason for this explosive yet ceremonially controlled manifestation, and furnish an explanation of the dovetailing of Events in subsequent years with His word written and published. In any case, whatever "Aiwaz" is, "Aiwaz" is an Intelligence possessed of power and knowledge absolutely beyond human experience; and therefore Aiwaz is a Being worthy, as the current use of the word allows, of the title of a God, yea verily and amen, of a God. Man has no such fact recorded, by proof established in surety beyond cavil of critic, as this Book, to witness the existence of an Intelligence praeterhuman and articulate, purposefully interfering in the philosophy, religion, ethics, economics and politics of the Planet.

The proof of His praeterhuman Nature—call Him a Devil or a God or even an Elemental as you will—is partly external, depending on events and persons without the sphere of Its influence, partly internal, depending on the concealment of

[1] Such a theory would further imply that I am, unknown to myself, possessed of all sorts of praeternatural knowledge and power. The law of Parsimony of Thought (Sir W. Hamilton) appears in rebuttal. Aiwaz calls Himself "the minister of Hoor-paar-Kraat," the twin of Heru-Ra-Ha. This is the dual form of Horus, child of Isis and Osiris.

(a) certain Truths, some previously known, some not known, but for the most part beyond the scope of my mind at the time of writing, (b) of an harmony of letters and numbers subtle, delicate and exact, and (c) of Keys to all life's mysteries, both pertinent to occult science and otherwise, and to all the Locks of Thought ; the concealment of these three galaxies of glory, I say, in a cipher simple and luminous, but yet illegible for over Fourteen years, and translated even then not by me, but by my mysterious Child according to the Foreknowledge written in the Book itself, in terms so complex that the exact fulfilment of the conditions of His birth, which occurred with incredible precision, seemed beyond all possibility, a cipher involving higher mathematics, and a knowledge of the Hebrew, Greek and Arabic Qabalahs as well as the True Lost Word of the Freemason, is yet veiled within the casual silk-stuff of ordinary English words, nay, even in the apparently accidental circumstance of the characters of the haste-harried scrawl of My pen.

Many such cases of double entendre, paranomasia in one language or another, sometimes two at once, numerical-literal puzzles, and even (on one occasion) an illuminating connexion of letters in various lines by a slashing scratch, will be found in the Qabalistic section of the Commentary.[1]

III

As an example of the first method above mentioned, we have, Cap. III, " The fool readeth this Book—and he understandeth it not." This has a secret reverse-sense, meaning :

[1] In preparation.

The fool (Parzival=Fra.O.I.V.V.I.O.) understandeth it (being a Magister Templi, the Grade attributed to Understanding) not (i.e. to be 'not').

This Parzival, adding to 418, is (in the legend of the Graal) the son of Kamuret, adding to 666, being the son of me The Beast by the Scarlet Woman Hilarion. This was a Name chosen by her when half drunk, as a theft from Theosophical legend, but containing many of our letter-number Keys to the Mysteries; the number of the petals in the most sacred lotus. It adds to 1001, which also is Seven times Eleven times Thirteen, a series of factors which may be read as The Scarlet Woman's Love by Magick producing Unity, in Hebrew Achad. For 7 is the number of Venus, and the secret seven-lettered Name of my concubine B A B A L O N is written with Seven Sevens, thus:

$$77+\frac{7+7}{7}+77=156,$$ the number of BABALON.

418 is the number of the Word of the Magical Formula of this Aeon. (666 is I, The Beast.)

Parzival had also the name Achad as a Neophyte of A.·.A.·., and it was Achad whom Hilarion bare to Me. And Achad means Unity, and the letter of Unity is Aleph, the letter of The Fool in the Tarot. Now this Fool invoked the Magical Formula of the Aeon by taking as his Magick, or True, Name, one which added also to 418.

He took it for his Name on Entering the Gnosis where is Understanding, and he understood it—this Book—not. That is, he understood that this Book was, so to speak, a vesture or veil upon the idea of "not." In Hebrew "not" is LA, 31, and AL is God, 31, while there is a third 31 still deeplier hidden in the double letter ST, which is a graphic glyph of the sun and moon conjoined to look like a foreshortened Phallus, thus — when written in Greek capitals. This S or Sigma is like a phallus, thus, σ, when writ small; and like a serpent or spermatozoon when writ final, thus, ς. This T or Theta is the point in the circle, or phallus in the kteis, and also the Sun just as C is the Moon, male and female.

But Sigma in Hebrew is Shin, 300, the letter of Fire and of the "Spirit of the Gods" which broods upon the Formless Void in the Beginning, being by shape a triple tongue of flame, and by meaning a tooth, which is the only part of the secret and solid foundation of Man that is manifested normally. Teeth serve him to fight, to crush, to cut, to rend, to bite and grip his prey; they witness that he is a fierce, dangerous, and carnivorous animal. But they are also the best witness to the mastery of Spirit over Matter, the extreme hardness of their substance being chiselled and polished and covered with a glistening film by Life no less easily and beautifully than it does with more naturally plastic types of substance.

Teeth are displayed when our Secret Self—our Subconscious Ego, whose Magical Image is our individuality expressed in mental and bodily form—our Holy Guardian Angel—comes forth and declares our True Will to our fellows, whether to snarl or to sneer, to smile or to laugh.

Teeth serve us to pronounce the dental letters which in their deepest nature express decision, fortitude, endurance, just as gutturals suggest the breath of Life itself free-flowing, and labials the duplex vibrations of action and reaction. Pronounce T, D, S or N, and you will find them all continuously forcible exhalations whose difference is determined solely by the position of the tongue, the teeth being bared as when a wild beast turns to bay. The sibilant sound of S or Sh is our English word, and also the Hebrew word, Hush, a strongly aspirated S, and suggests the hiss of a snake. Now this hiss is the common sign of recognition between men when one wants to call another's attention without disturbing the silence more than necessary. (Also we have Hist, our Double letter.) This hiss means: "Attention! A man!" For in all Semitic and some Aryan languages, ISh or a closely similar word means "a man." Say it: you must bare your clenched teeth as in defiance, and breathe harshly out as in excitement.

Hiss! Sh! means "Keep silent! there's danger if you are heard. Attention! There's a man somewhere, deadly as a snake. Breathe hard; there's a fight coming."

This Sh is then the forcible subtle creative Spirit of Life, fiery and triplex, continuous, Silence of pure Breath modified into sound by two and thirty obstacles, as the Zero of Empty Space, though it contain all Life, only takes form according (as the Qabalists say) to the two and thirty "Paths" of Number and Letter which obstruct it.

Now the other letter, Theta or Teth, has the value of Nine, which is that of AVB, the Secret Magick of Obeah, and of the Sephira Yesod, which is the seat in man of the sexual function by whose Magick he overcomes even Death, and that in more ways than one, ways that are known to none but the loftiest and most upright Initiates, baptised by the Baptism of Wisdom, and communicants at that Eucharist where the Fragment of the Host in the Chalice becomes whole.[1]

[1] The Chalice is not presented to laymen. Those who understand the reason for this and other details of the Mass, will wonder at the perfection with which the Roman Communion has preserved the form, and lost the substance, of the Supreme Magical Ritual of the True Gnosis.

This T is the letter of Leo, the Lion, the house of heaven sacred to the Sun. (Thus also we find in it the number 6, whence 666). And Teth means a Serpent, the symbol of the magical Life of the Soul, lord of " the double wand " of life and death. The serpent is royal, hooded, wise, silent save for an hiss when need is to disclose his Will ; he devours his tail—the glyph of Eternity, of Nothingness and of Space ; he moves wavelike, one immaterial essence travelling through crest and trough, as a man's soul through lives and deaths. He straightens out ; he is the Rod that strikes, the Light-radiance of the Sun or the Life-radiance of the Phallus.

The sound of T is tenuous and sharply final ; it suggests a spontaneous act sudden and irrevocable, like the snake's bite, the lion's snap, the Sun's stroke, and the Lingam's.

Now in the Tarot the Trump illustrating this letter Sh is an old form of the Stèlè of Revealing, Nuith with Shu and Seb, the pantacle or magical picture of the old Aeon, as Nuit with Hadit and Ra Hoor Khuit is of the new. The number of this Trump is XX. It is called the Angel, the messenger from Heaven of the new Word. The Trump giving the picture of T is called Strength. Its number is XI. It shows the Scarlet Woman, BABALON, riding (or conjoined with) me The Beast; and this card is my special card, for I am Baphomet, "the Lion and the Serpent," and 666, the " full number " of the Sun.[1]

So then, as Sh, XX, shows the Gods of the Book of the Law and T, XI, shows the human beings in that Book, me and my concubine, the two cards together illustrate the whole Book in pictorial form.

[1] The "magical numbers" of the Sun are, according to tradition, 6, (6 x 6) 36, (666 ÷ 6) 111, and $\sum$ (1–36) 666.

Now XX+XI=XXXI, 31, the third 31, which we needed to put with LA, 31 and AL, 31, that we might have 31×3=93, the Word of the Law, θελημα, Will, and ἀγαπη, Love which under Will, is the Law. It is also the number of Aiwaz, the Author of the Book, of the Lost Word whose formula does in sober truth " raise Hiram," and of many another close-woven Word of Truth.

Now then this Two-in-One letter ☾☉, is the third Key to this Law ; and on the discovery of that fact, after years of constant seeking, what sudden splendours of Truth, sacred as secret, blazed in the midnight of my mind.! Observe now : " this circle squared in its failure is a key also." Now I knew that in the value of the letters of ALHIM, " the Gods," the Jews had concealed a not quite correct value of π, the ratio of a circle's circumference to its diameter, to 4 places of decimals : 3.1415 ; nearer would be 3.1416. If I prefix our Key, 31, putting ☾☉, Set or Satan, before the old Gods, I get 3.141593, π correct to Six places, Six being my own number and that of Horus the Sun. And the whole number of this new Name is 395,[1] which on analysis yields an astounding cluster of numerical " mysteries."

IV

Now for an example of the 'paronomasia' or pun. Chapter III, 16 — " Ye, even ye, know not this meaning all. " (Note how the peculiar grammar suggests a hidden meaning.) Now YE is in Hebrew Yod Hé, the man and the woman;

[1] Shin 300 Teth 9 Aleph 1 Lamed 30 He 5 Yod 10 Mem 40. Note that 395 is to be reversed, 593 being the correction required ! Note also the 31 and the 93 in this value of π .

The Beast and BABALON, whom the God was addressing in his verse. Know suggests 'no' which gives LA, 31; 'not' is LA, 31, again, by actual meaning; and 'all' refers to AL, 31, again. (Again, ALL is 61, AIN, "nothing.")

V

Then we have numerical problems like this. "Six and fifty. Divide, add, multiply and understand." 6÷50 gives 0·12, a perfect glyph-statement of the metaphysics of the Book.

The external evidence for the Book is accumulating yearly: the incidents connected with the discovery of the true spelling of Aiwaz are alone sufficient to place it beyond all quaver of doubt that I am really in touch with a Being of intelligence and power immensely subtler and greater than aught we can call human.

This has been the One Fundamental Question of Religion. We know of invisible powers, and to spare! But is there any Intelligence or Individuality (of the same general type as ours) independent of our human brain-structure? For the first time in history, yes! Aiwaz has given us proof: the most important gate toward Knowledge swings wide.

I, Aleister Crowley, declare upon my honour as a gentleman that I hold this revelation a million times more important than the discovery of the Wheel, or even of the Laws of Physics or Mathematics. Fire and Tools made Man master of his planet: Writing developed his mind; but his Soul was a guess until the Book of the Law proved this.

I, a master of English, was made to take down in three

hours, from dictation, sixty-five 8″ x 10″ pages of words not only strange, but often displeasing to me in themselves ; concealing in cipher propositions unknown to me, majestic and profound ; foretelling events public and private beyond my control, or that of any man.

This Book proves : there is a Person thinking and acting in a praeterhuman manner, either without a body of flesh, or with the power of communicating telepathically with men and inscrutably directing their actions.

VI

I write this therefore with a sense of responsibility so acute that for the first time in my life I regret my sense of humour and the literary practical jokes which it has caused me to perpetrate. I am glad, though, that care was taken of the MS. itself and of diaries and letters of the period, so that the physical facts are as plain as can be desired.

My sincerity and seriousness are proved by my life. I have fought this Book and fled it ; I have defiled it and I have suffered for its sake. Present or absent to my mind, it has been my Invisible Ruler. It has overcome me ; year after year extends its invasion of my being. I am the captive of the Crowned and Conquering Child.

The point then arises : How did the Book of the Law come to be written ? The description in The Equinox, I, VII, might well be more detailed ; and I might also elucidate the problem of the apparent changes of speaker, and the occasional lapses from straightforward scribecraft in the MS.

I may observe that I should not have left such obvious

grounds for indictment as these had I prepared the MS. to look pretty to a critical eye ; nor should I have left such curious deformities of grammar and syntax, defects of rhythm, and awkwardness of phrase. I should not have printed passages, some rambling and unintelligible, some repugnant to reason by their absurdity, others again by their barbaric ferocity abhorrent to heart. I should not have allowed such jumbles of matter, such abrupt jerks from subject to subject, disorder ravaging reason with disconnected sluttishness. I should not have tolerated the discords, jarred and jagged, of manner, as when a sublime panegyric of Death is followed first by a cipher and then by a prophecy, before, without taking breath, the author leaps to the utmost magnificence of thought both mystical and practical, in language so concise, simple, and lyrical as to bemuse our very amazement. I should not have spelt " Ay " " Aye," or acquiesced in the horror " abstruction."

Compare with this Book my " jokes," where I pretend to edit the MS. of another : " Alice," " Amphora," " Clouds without Water." Observe in each case the technical perfection of the " discovered " or " translated " MS., smooth skilled elaborate art and craft of a Past Master Workman ; observe the carefully detailed tone and style of the prefaces, and the sedulous creation of the personalities of the imaginary author and the imaginary editor.

Note, moreover, with what greedy vanity I claim authorship even of all the other A.·.A.·. Books in Class A, though I wrote them inspired beyond all I know to be I. Yet in these Books did Aleister Crowley, the master of English both in prose and in verse, partake insofar as he was That. Compare those Books with the Book of the Law! The style is simple and sublime; the imagery is gorgeous and faultless; the rhythm is subtle and intoxicating; the theme is interpreted in faultless symphony. There are no errors of grammar, no infelicities of phrase. Each Book is perfect in its kind.[1]

I, daring to snatch credit for these, in that brutal Index to The Equinox Volume One, dared nowise to lay claim to have touched the Book of the Law, not with my littlest finger-tip.

I, boasting of my many Books; I, swearing each a masterpiece; I attack the Book of the Law at a dozen points of literature. Even so, with the same breath, I testify, as a Master of English, that I am utterly incapable, even when most inspired, of such English as I find in that Book again and again.

Terse, yet sublime, are these verses of this Book; subtle yet simple; matchless for rhythm, direct as a ray of light. Its imagery is gorgeous without decadence. It deals with primary ideas. It announces revolutions in philosophy, religion, ethics, yea, in the whole nature of Man. For this it needs no more than to roll sea-billows solemnly forth, eight words, as '*Every man and every woman is a star,*" or it bursts in a mountain torrent of monosyllables as "*Do what thou wilt shall be the whole of the Law.*"

Nuith cries: "*I love you,*" like a lover; when even John reached only to the cold impersonal proposition "God is love." She woos like a mistress; whispers "*To me!*" in every ear; Jesus, with needless verb, appeals vehemently to them "that labour and are heavy laden." Yet he can promise

[1] See Liber LXV, I, Equinox III, and Liber VII Equinox III, II, especially.

no more than "I will give you rest," in the future; while Nuit, in the present, says: *"I give unimaginable joys on earth,"* making life worth while; *"certainty, not faith, while in life, upon death,"* the electric light Knowledge for the churchyard corpse-candle Faith, making life fear-free, and death itself worth while: *"peace unutterable, rest, ecstasy,"* making mind and body at ease that soul may be free to transcend them when It will.

I have never written such English; nor could I ever, that well I know. Shakespeare could not have written it: still less could Keats, Shelley, Swift, Sterne or even Wordsworth. Only in the Books of Job and Ecclesiastes, in the work of Blake, or possibly in that of Poe, is there any approach to such succinct depth of thought in such musical simplicity of form, unless it be in Greek and Latin poets. Nor Poe nor Blake could have sustained their effort as does this our Book of the Law; and the Hebrews used tricks of verse, mechanical props to support them.

How then—back once more to the Path!—how then did it come to be written?

VIII

I shall make what I may call an inventory of the furniture of the Temple, the circumstances of the case. I shall describe the conditions of the phenomenon as if it were any other unexplained event in Nature.

1. The time.

    Chapter I was written between Noon and 1 p.m. on April 8, 1904.

Chapter II between Noon and 1 p.m. on April 9, 1904.

Chapter III between Noon and 1 p.m. on April 10, 1904.

The writing began exactly on the stroke of the hour, and ended exactly an hour later; it was hurried throughout, with no pauses of any kind.

2. The place.

The city was Cairo.

The street, or rather streets, I do not remember. There is a 'Place' where four or five streets intersect; it is near the Boulak Museum, but a fairly long way from Shepherd's. The quarter is fashionably European. The house occupied a corner. I do not remember its orientation; but, as appears from the instructions for invoking Horus, one window of the temple opened to the East or North. The apartment was of several rooms on the ground floor, well furnished in the Anglo-Egyptian style. It was let by a firm named Congdon & Co.

The room was a drawing-room cleared of fragile obstacles, but not otherwise prepared to serve as a temple. It had double doors, opening on to the corridor to the North and a door to the East leading to another room, the dining-room, I think. It had two windows opening on the Place, to the South, and a writing table against the wall between them.

3. The people.

A. Myself, age 28½. In good health, fond of out-door sports, especially mountaineering and big-game shooting. An Adept Major of the A.·.A.·., but weary of mysticism and dissatisfied with Magick. A rationalist, Buddhist, agnostic, anti-clerical, anti-moral, Tory and Jacobite. A chess-player, first-class amateur, able to play three games simultaneously blindfold. A reading and writing addict. Education : private governess and tutors, preliminary school Habershon's at St. Leonards, Sussex, private tutors, private school 51 Bateman St., Cambridge, private tutors, Yarrow's School, Streatham, near London. Malvern College, Tonbridge School, private tutors, Eastbourne College, King's College, London, Trinity College, Cambridge.

Morality—Sexually powerful and passionate. Strongly male to women ; free from any similar impulse toward my own sex. My passion for women very unselfish ; the main motive to give them pleasure. Hence, intense ambition to understand the feminine nature ; for this purpose, to identify myself with their feelings, and to use all means appropriate. Imaginative, subtle, insatiable ; the whole business a mere clumsy attempt to quench the thirst of the soul. This thirst has indeed been my one paramount Lord, directing all my acts without allowing any other considerations soever to affect it in the least.

Strictly temperate as to drink, had never once been even near intoxication. Light wine my only form of alcohol.

General morality that of a normal aristocrat.

Sense of justice and equity so sensitive, well-balanced and compelling as to be almost an obsession.

Generous, unless suspicious that I was being fleeced : " penny wise and pound foolish." Spendthrift, careless, not a gambler because I valued winning at games of skill, which flattered my vanity.

Kind, gentle, affectionate, selfish, conceited, reckless and cautious by turns.

Incapable of bearing a grudge, even for the gravest insults and injuries; yet enjoying to inflict pain for its own sake. Can attack an unsuspecting stranger, and torture him cruelly for years, without feeling the slightest animosity toward him. Fond of animals and children, who return my love, almost always. Consider abortion the most shameful form of murder, and loathe the social codes which encourage it.

Hated and despised my mother and her family; loved and respected my father and his.

Critical events in my life.

First travelled outside England, 1883.

Father died March 5, 1887.

Albuminuria stopped my schooling, 1890-92.

First sexual act, probably 1889.

Ditto with a woman March, 1891 (Torquay—a theatre girl).

First serious mountain-climbing, in Skye, 1892. (The "Pinnacle Ridge" of Sgurr-nan-Gillean.)

First Alpine climb, 1894.

Admitted to the Military Order of the Temple midnight, December 31, 1896.

Admitted to permanent office in the Temple midnight, December 31, 1897.

Bought Boleskine, 1899.

First Mexican climb, 1900.

First Big game, 1901.

First Himalayan climb, 1902. (Chogo Ri, or "K2" expedition.)

Married at Dingwall, Scotland, August 12, 1903.

Honeymoon at Boleskine, thence to London, Paris, Naples, Egypt, Ceylon, and back to Egypt, Helwan and then Cairo early in 1904.

My " occult " career.

Parents Plymouth Brethren, exclusive.

Father a real P.B. and therefore tolerant to his son.

Mother only became P.B. to please him, perhaps to catch him, and so pedantically fanatical.

After his death I was tortured with insensate persistency, till I said: Evil, be thou my good! I practised wickedness furtively as a magical formula, even when it was distasteful; e.g. I would sneak into a church[1]—a place my mother would not enter at the funeral service of her best-loved sister.

Revolted openly when puberty gave me a moral sense.

Hunted new " Sins " till October, '97, when one of them turned to bay, and helped me to experience the " Trance of Sorrow." (Perception of the Impermanence of even the greatest human endeavour.) I invoked assistance, Easter, '98.

Initiated in the Hermetic Order of the Golden Dawn, November 18, '98.

Began to perform the Abramelin Operation, 1899.

Initiated in the Order R.R. et A.C., January, 1909.

Made a 33° Freemason, 1900.

Began Yoga practices, 1900.

Obtained first Dhyana, October 1, 1901.

Abandoned all serious occult work of every sort, October 3, 1901, and continued in this course of action till July, 1903,

[1] Church of England. I confidently supposed that Anglicanism was a peculiarly violent form of Devil-Worship, and was in despair at being unable to discover where the Abomination came in.

when I tried vainly to force myself to become a Buddhist Hermit Highland Laird.

Marriage was an uninterrupted sexual debauch up to the time of the writing of the Book of the Law.

B. Rose Edith Kelly.

Born 1874 (July 23). About '95 married one Major Skerrett, R.A.M.C., and lived with him some two years in South Africa. He died in '97.

She indulged in a few feebly-executed intrigues till August 12, 1903, when she became my wife, becoming pregnant with a girl born July 28, 1904. Health, admirably robust at all points; she was both active and enduring, as our travels in Ceylon and across China prove. Figure perfect, neither big nor little, face pretty without being petty; she only missed Beauty by lacking Goethe's "touch of the bizarre." Personality intensely powerful and magnetic, intellect absent but mind adaptable to that of any companion, so that she could always say the right nothing.

Charm, grace, vitality, vivacity, tact, manners, all inexpressibly fascinating.

From her mother she inherited dipsomania, as bad a case for stealth, cunning, falsehood, treachery, and hypocrisy as the specialist I consulted had ever known. This was, however, latent during the satisfaction of sexuality,[1] which ousted all else in her life, as it did in mine.

Education strictly social and domestic; she did not even know schoolgirl French. She had read nothing, not so much as novels. She was a miracle of perfection as Poetic Ideal,

[1] It broke out during my absence (1906), and made it impossible to resume the previous relations.

Mistress, Wife, Mother, House-president, Nurse, Pal and Comrade.

C. Our head servant, Hassan or Hamid, I forget which.

A tall, dignified, handsome athlete of about 30. Spoke good English and ran the household well ; always there and never in the way.

I suppose I hardly ever saw the servants under his authority : I do not even know how many there were.

D. Lieut.-Col. Somebody, beginning, I think, with a B, married, middle-aged, with manners like the Rules of a Prison. I cannot remember that I ever saw him ; but the apartment was sublet to me by him.

E. Brugsch Bey of the Boulak Museum dined with us once to discuss the Stélé in his charge, and to arrange for its " abstruction." His French assistant curator, who translated the hieroglyphs on the Stélé for us.

A Mr. Back, owner of the " Egyptian News," an hotel, a hunk of railway, &c., &c., dined once.

Otherwise we knew nobody in Cairo except natives, occasionally hobnobbed with a General Dickson, who had accepted Islam, carpet merchants, pimps, jewellers, and such small deer. Contradictory hints in one of my diaries were inserted deliberately to mislead, for some silly no-reason unconnected with Magick.[1]

4. The events leading up to the Writing of the Book. I summarize them from Eqx. I, VII.

[1] See previous chapter.

March 16. Tried to shew the Sylphs to Rose.[1] She was in a dazed state, stupid, possibly drunk ; possibly hysterical from pregnancy. She could see nothing, but could hear. She was fiercely excited at the messages, and passionately insistent that I should take them seriously.

I was annoyed at her irrelevance, and her infliction of nonsense upon me.

She had never been in any state even remotely resembling this, though I had made the same invocation (in full) in the King's chamber of the Great Pyramid during the night which we spent there in the previous autumn.

March 17. More apparently nonsensical messages, this time spontaneous. I invoked Thoth, probably as in Liber LXIV, and presumably to clear up the muddle.

March 18. Thoth evidently got clear through to her ; for she discovers that Horus is addressing me through her, and identifies Him by a method utterly excluding chance or coincidence, and involving knowledge which only I possessed, some of it arbitrary, so that she or her informant must have been able to read my mind as well as if I had spoken it.

Then she, challenged to point out His image, passes by many such to fix on the one in the Stélé. The cross-examination must have taken place between March 20 and 23.

March 20. Success in my invocation of Horus, by " breaking all the rules " at her command. This success convinced me magically, and encouraged me to test her as above mentioned. I should certainly have referred to the Stélé in my ritual had I seen it before this date. I should fix Monday, March 21, for the Visit to Boulak.

[1] I invoked them by the Air section of Liber Samekh, and the appropriate God-names, Pentagrams, &c.

Between March 23 and April 8 the Hieroglyphs on the Stélé were evidently translated by the assistant-curator at Boulak, into either French or English—I am almost sure it was French—and versified (as now printed) by me.

Between these dates, too, my wife must have told me that her informant was not Horus, or Ra Hoor Khuit, but a messenger from Him, named Aiwass.

I thought that she might have faked this name from constantly hearing "Aiwa," the word for "Yes" in Arabic. She could not have invented a name of this kind, though; her next best was to find a phrase like "balmy puppy" for a friend, or corrupt a name like Neuberg into an obscene insult.

The silence of my diaries seems to prove that she gave me nothing more of importance. I was working out the Magical problem presented to me by the events of March 16-21. Any questions that I asked her were either unanswered, or answered by a Being whose mind was so different from mine that we failed to converse. All my wife obtained from Him was to command me to do things magically absurd. He would not play my game: I must play His.

April 7. Not later than this date was I ordered to enter the "temple" exactly at noon on the three days following, and write down what I heard during one hour, nor more nor less. I imagine that some preparations were made, possibly some precautions against disturbance, possibly some bull's blood burned for incense, or order taken about details of dress or diet; I remember nothing at all, one way or the other. Bull's blood was burnt some time in this sojourn in Cairo; but I forget why or when. I think it was used at the "Invocation of the Sylphs."

5. The actual writing.

The three days were precisely similar, save that on the last day I became nervous lest I should fail to hear the Voice of Aiwass. They may then be described all together.

I went into the " temple " a minute early, so as to shut the door and sit down on the stroke of Noon.

On my table were my pen—a Swan Fountain—and supplies of Quarto typewriting paper, 8″ x 10″.

I never looked round in the room at any time.

The Voice of Aiwass came apparently from over my left shoulder, from the furthest corner of the room. It seemed to echo itself in my physical heart in a very strange manner, hard to describe. I have noticed a similar phenomenon when I have been waiting for a message fraught with great hope or dread. The voice was passionately poured, as if Aiwass were alert about the time-limit. I wrote 65 pages of this present essay (at about my usual rate of composition) in about $10\frac{1}{2}$ hours as against the 3 hours of the 65 pages of the Book of the Law. I was pushed hard to keep the pace ; the MS. shows it clearly enough.

The voice was of deep timbre, musical and expressive, its tones solemn, voluptuous, tender, fierce or aught else as suited the moods of the message. Not bass—perhaps a rich tenor or baritone.

The English was free of either native or foreign accent, perfectly pure of local or caste mannerisms, thus startling and even uncanny at first hearing.[1]

[1] The effect was thus as if the language were " English-in-itself," without any background, such as exists when one hears any one human speak it, and enables one to assign all sorts of attributes to the speaker.

I had a strong impression[1] that the speaker was actually in the corner where he seemed to be, in a body of "fine matter," transparent as a veil of gauze, or a cloud of incense-smoke. He seemed to be a tall, dark man in his thirties, well-knit, active and strong, with the face of a savage king, and eyes veiled lest their gaze should destroy what they saw. The dress was not Arab; it suggested Assyria or Persia, but very vaguely. I took little note of it, for to me at that time Aiwass was an "angel" such as I had often seen in visions, a being purely astral.

I now incline to believe that Aiwass is not only the God or Demon or Devil once held holy in Sumer, and mine own Guardian Angel, but also a man as I am, insofar as He uses a human body to make His magical link with Mankind, whom He loves, and that He is thus an Ipsissimus, the Head of the A.·.A.·. Even I can do, in a much feebler way, this Work of being a God and a Beast, &c., &c., all at the same time, with equal fullness of life.[2]

6. The Editing of the Book.

"Change not so much as the style of a letter" in the text saved me from Crowley-fying the whole Book, and spoiling everything.

The MS. shows what has been done, and why, as follows:

[1] This impression seems to have been a sort of visualization in the imagination. It is not uncommon for me to receive intimations in this manner.

[2] I do not necessarily mean that he is a member of human society in quite the normal way. He might rather be able to form for Himself a human body as circumstances indicate, from the appropriate Elements, and dissolve it when the occasion for its use is past. I say this because I have been permitted to see Him in recent years in a variety of physical appearances, all equally "material" in the sense in which my own body is so.

A. On page 6 Aiwaz instructs me to " write this (what he had just said) in whiter words," for my mind rebelled at His phrase. He added at once " But go forth on," i.e., with His utterance, leaving the emendation until later.

B. On page 19 I failed to hear a sentence, and (later on) the Scarlet Woman, invoking Aiwass, wrote in the missing words. (How? She was not in the room at the time, and heard nothing.)

C. Page 20 of Cap. III, I got a phrase indistinctly, and she put it in, as for " B."

D. The versified paraphrase of the hieroglyphs on the Stélé being ready, Aiwaz allowed me to insert these later, so as to save time.

These four apart, the MS. is exactly as it was written on those three days. The Critical Recension will explain these points as they occur.

IX

The problem of the literary form of this Book is astonishingly complex; but the internal evidence of the sense is usually sufficient to make it clear, on inspection, as to who is speaking and who is being addressed.

There was, however, no actual voice audible save that of Aiwaz. Even my own remarks made silently were incorporated by him audibly, wherever such occur.

CHAPTER I

Verse 1. Nuit is the speaker. She invokes her lover and then begins to give a title to her speech in the end of verse 1—20.

In verses 3 and 4, she begins her discourse. So far her remarks have been addressed to no one in particular.

Verse 4 startled my intelligence into revolt.

In verse 5 she explains that she is speaking, and appeals to me personally to help her to unveil by taking down her message.

In verse 6 she claims me for her chosen, and I think that I then became afraid lest I should be expected to do too much. She answers this fear in verse 7 by introducing Aiwaz as the actual speaker in articulate human accents on her behalf.

In verse 8 the oration continues, and we now see that it is addressed to mankind in general. This continues till verse 13.

Verse 14 is from the Stélé. It seems to have been written in by me as a kind of appreciation of what she had just said.

Verse 15 emphasizes that it is mankind in general that is addressed; for the Beast is spoken of in the third person, though his was the only human ear to hear the words.

Verses 18—19 seem to be almost in the nature of a quotation from some hymn. It is not quite natural for her to address herself as she appears to do in verse 19.

Verse 26. The question "Who am I and what shall be the sign?" is my own conscious thought. In the previous verses I have been called to an exalted mission, and I naturally feel nervous. This thought is then entered in the record by Aiwaz as if it were a story that he was telling; and he develops this story after her answer, in order to bring back the thread of the chapter to the numerical mysteries of Nuith begun in verses 24-25, and now continued in verse 28.

Another doubt must have arisen in my mind at verse 30; and this doubt is interpreted and explained to me personally in verse 31.

The address to mankind is resumed in verse 32, and Nuith emphasizes the point of verse 30 which has caused me to doubt. She confirms this with an oath, and I was convinced. I thought to myself, "in this case let us have written instructions as to the technique," and Aiwaz again makes a story out of my request as in verse 26.

In verse 35 it seems that she is addressing me personally, but in verse 36 she speaks of me in the third person.

Verse 40. The word "us" is very puzzling. It apparently means "All those who have accepted the Law whose word is Thelema." Among these she includes herself.

There is now no difficulty for a long while. It is a general address dealing with various subjects, to the end of verse 52.

From verses 53-56 we have a strictly personal address to me.

In verse 57 Nuith resumes her general exhortation. And I am spoken of once more in the third person.

Verse 61. The word "Thou" is not a personal address. It means any single person, as opposed to a company. The "Ye" in the third sentence indicates the proper conduct for worshippers as a body. The "you," in sentence 4, of course applies to a single person; but the plural form suggests that it is a matter of public worship as opposed to the invocation in the desert of the first sentence of this verse.

There is no further difficulty in this chapter.

Verse 66 is the statement of Aiwaz that the words of verse 65, which were spoken diminuendo down to pianissimo, indicated the withdrawal of the goddess.

CHAPTER II

Hadith himself is evidently the speaker from the start. The remarks are general. In verse 5 I am spoken of in the third person.

After verse 9 he notices my vehement objections to writing statements to which my conscious self was obstinately opposed.

Verse 10, addressed to me, notes that fact; and in verse 11 he declares that he is my master, and that the reason for this is that he is my secret self, as explained in verses 12-13.

The interruption seems to have added excitement to the discourse, for verse 14 is violent.

Verses 15 & 16 offer a riddle, while verse 17 is a sort of parody of poetry.

Verse 18 continues his attack on my conscious mind. In verses 15-18 the style is complicated, brutal, sneering and jeering. I feel the whole passage as a contemptuous beating down of the resistance of my mind.

In verse 19 he returns to the exalted style with which he began until I interfered.

The passage seems addressed to what he calls his chosen or his people, though it is not explained exactly what he means by the words.

This passage from verse 19 to verse 52 is of sustained and matchless eloquence.

I must have objected to something in verse 52, for verse 53 is directed to encourage me personally as to having transmitted this message.

Verse 54 deals with another point as to the intelligibility of the message.

Verse 55 instructed me to obtain the English Qabalah; it made me incredulous, as the task seemed an impossible one, and probably his perception of this criticism inspired verse 56, though "ye mockers" applies evidently to my enemies, referred to in verse 54.

Verse 57 brings us back to the subject begun in verse 21. It is a quotation from the Apocalypse verbatim, and is probably suggested by the matter of verse 56.

There is no real change in the essence of anything, however its combinations vary.

Verses 58-60 conclude the passage.

Verse 61. The address is now strictly personal. During all this time Hadith had been breaking down my resistance with his violently expressed and varied phrases. As a result of this, I attained to the trance described in these verses from 61-68.

Verse 69 is the return to consciousness of myself. It was a sort of gasping question as a man coming out of Ether might ask "Where am I?" I think that this is the one passage in the whole book which was not spoken by Aiwaz; and I ought to say that these verses 63-68 were written without conscious hearing at all.

Verse 70 does not deign to reply to my questions, but points out the way to manage life. This continues until verse 74, and seems to be addressed not to me personally but to any man, despite the use of the word "Thou."

Verse 75 abruptly changes the subject, interpolating the riddle of verse 76 with its prophecy. This verse is addressed to me personally, and continues to the end of verse 78 to mingle lyrical eloquence with literal and numerical puzzles.

Verse 79 is the statement of Aiwaz that the end of the chapter has come. To this he adds his personal compliment to myself.

CHAPTER III

Verse 1 appears to complete the triangle begun by the first verses of the two previous chapters. It is a simple statement involving no particular speaker or hearer. The omission of the "i" in the name of the God appears to have alarmed me, and in verse 2 Aiwaz offers a hurried explanation in a somewhat excited manner, and invokes Ra-Hoor-Khuit.

Verse 3 is spoken by Ra-Hoor-Khuit. " Them " evidently refers to some undescribed enemies, and " ye " to those who accept his formula. This passage ends with verse 9. Verse 10 and verse 11 are addressed to me personally and the Scarlet Woman, as shown in the continuation of this passage which seems to end with verse 33, though it is left rather vague at times as to whether the Beast, or the Beast and his Concubine, or the adherents of Horus, generally, are exhorted.

Verse 34 is a kind of poetical peroration, and is not addressed in particular to anybody. It is a statement of events to come.

Verse 35 states simply that section one of this chapter is completed.

I seem to have become enthusiastic, for there is a kind of interlude reported by Aiwaz of my song of adoration translated from the Stélé; the incident parallels that of Chapter I, verse 26, &c.

It is to be noted that the translations from the Stélé in verses 37-38 were no more than instantaneous thoughts to be inserted afterwards.

Verse 38 begins with my address to the God in the first sentence, while in the second is his reply to me. He then refers to the hieroglyphs of the Stélé, and bids me quote my paraphrases. This order was given by a species of wordless gesture, not visible nor audible, but sensible in some occult manner.

Verses 39-42 are instructions for me personally.

Verses 43-45 indicate the proper course of conduct for the Scarlet Woman.

Verse 46 is again more general—a sort of address to soldiers before battle.

Verse 47 is again mostly personal instruction, mixed up with prophecies, proof of the praeterhuman origin of the Book, and other matters.

I observe that this instruction, taken with those not to change "so much as the style of a letter," etc., imply that my pen was under the physical control of Aiwaz; for his dictation did not include directions as to the use of capitals, and the occasional mis-spellings are most assuredly not mine!

Verse 48 impatiently dismisses such practical matters as a nuisance.

Verses 49-59 contain a series of declarations of war; and there is no further difficulty as to speaker or hearer to the end of the chapter, although the subject changes repeatedly in an incomprehensible manner. Only in verse 75 do we find a peroration on the whole book, presumably by Aiwaz, ending by his formula of withdrawal.

I conclude by laying down the principles of Exegesis on which I have based my comment.[1]

1. It is " my scribe Ankh-af-na-khonsu " (CCXX, I, 36) who " shall comment " on " this book " " by the wisdom of Ra-Hoor-Khuit " ; that is, Aleister Crowley shall write the Comment from the point of view of the manifested positive Lord of the Aeon, in plain terms of the finite, and not those of the infinite.

2. " Hadit burning in thy heart shall make swift and secure thy pen " (CCXX, III, 40). My own inspiration, not any alien advice or intellectual consideration, is to be the energizing force of this work.

3. Where the text is simple straightforward English, I shall not seek, or allow, any interpretation at variance with it.

I may admit a Qabalistic or cryptographic secondary meaning when such confirms, amplifies, deepens, intensifies, or clarifies the obvious common-sense significance ; but only if it be part of the general plan of the " latent light," and self-proven by abundant witness.

For example : " To me ! " (I, 65) is to be taken primarily in its obvious sense as the Call of Nuith to us Her stars.

The transliteration " TO MH " may be admitted as the " signature " of Nuith, identifying Her as the speaker ; be-

[1] The following passage, to the end of the chapter, refers to the Commentary ; whereas the Comment itself is printed, above, with the text. This Comment is the really inspired message, cutting as it does all the difficulties with a single keen stroke. We have decided, however, to retain the passage for its essential interest and as a preliminary to the publication of the Commentary—Ed.

cause these Greek Words mean " The Not," which is Her Name.

This Gematria of TO MH may be admitted as further confirmation, because their number 418 is elsewhere manifested as that of the Aeon.

But TO MH is not to be taken as negating the previous verses, or 418 as indicating the formula of approach to Her, although in point of fact it is so, being the Rubrick of the Great Work. I refuse to consider mere appropriateness as conferring title to authority, and to read my own personal theories into the Book. I insist that all interpretation shall be incontestably authentic, neither less, more, nor other than was meant in the Mind of Aiwaz.

4. I lay claim to be the sole authority competent to decide disputed points with regard to the Book of the Law, seeing that its Author, Aiwaz, is none other than mine own Holy Guardian Angel, to Whose Knowledge and Conversation I have attained, so that I have exclusive access to Him. I have duly referred every difficulty to Him directly, and received His answer ; my award is therefore absolute without appeal.

5. The verse, II, 47, " one cometh after him, whence I say not, who shall discover the key of it all," has been fulfilled by " one " Achad discovering the number 31 as the key in question. But the work of Achad is not said to extend beyond this single exploit ; Achad is nowhere indicated as appointed or even authorized to relieve The Beast of His task of the Comment. Achad has proved himself,[1] and proved the Book, by his one achievement ; and this shall suffice.

[1] I note that A Ch D is " his child " without reference to The Scarlet Woman ; whereas the Child who is to be " mightier than all the kings of the earth " is to be bred from Her, without reference to the Beast. There is no indication that these two children are not identical ; but there is none that they are. Hans " Carter " (or Hirsig) might perfectly well be the latter of these children.

6. Wherever
   - a. The words of the Text are obscure in themselves; where
   - b. The expression is strained; where
   - c. The Syntax,
   - d. Grammar,
   - e. Spelling, or
   - f. The use of capital letters present peculiarities; where
   - g. Non-English words occur; where the style suggests
   - h. Paronomasia,
   - i. Ambiguity, or
   - j. Obliquity; or where
   - k. A problem is explicitly declared to exist; in all such cases I shall seek for a meaning hidden by means of Qabalistic correspondences, cryptography, or literary subtleties. I shall admit no solution which is not at once simple, striking, consonant with the general plan of the Book; and not only adequate but necessary.

Examples:

- i I, 4. Here the obvious sense of the text is nonsense; it therefore needs intimate analysis.
- ii II, 17, line 4. The natural order of the words is distorted by placing "not" before "know me"; it is proper to ask what object is attained by this peculiarity of phrasing.
- iii I, 13. The text as it stands is unintelligible; it

calls attention to itself; a meaning must be found which will not only justify the apparent error, but prove the necessity of employing that and no other expression.

iv II, 76. " to be me " for " to be I." The unusual grammar invites enquiry; it suggests that " me " is a concealed name, perhaps MH, " Not," Nuith, since to be Nuith is the satisfaction of the formula of the Speaker, Hadith.

v III, 1. The omission of the " i " in " Khuit " is indicative that some concealed doctrine is based upon the variant.

vi II, 27. The spelling of " Because " with a capital B suggests that it may be a proper name, and possibly that its Greek or Hebrew equivalent may identify the idea Qabalistically with some enemy of our Hierarchy; also that such word may demand a capital value for its initial.

vii III, 11. " Abstruction " suggests that an idea otherwise inexpressible is conveyed in this manner. Paraphrase is here inadmissible as a sufficient interpretation; there must be a correspondence in the actual structure of the word with its etymologically-deduced meaning.

viii III, 74. The words " sun " and " son " are evidently chosen for the identity of their sound-value; the inelegance of the phrase therefore insists on some such adequate justification as the existence of a hidden treasure of meaning.

ix III, 73. The ambiguity of the instruction warrants the supposition that the words must somehow contain a cryptographic formula for so arranging the sheets of the MS. that an Arcanum becomes manifest.

x I, 26. The apparent evasion of a direct reply in "Thou knowest!" suggests that the words conceal a precise answer more convincing in cipher than their openly-expressed equvialent could be.

xi II, 15. The text explicitly invites Qabalistic analysis.

7. The Comment must be consistent with itself at all points; it must exhibit the Book of the Law as of absolute authority on all possible questions proper to Mankind, as offering the perfect solution of all problems philosophical and practical without exception.

8. The Comment must prove beyond possibility of error that the Book of the Law,

a. Bears witness in itself to the authorship of Aiwaz, an Intelligence independent of incarnation; and
b. Is warranted worthy of its claim to credence by the evidence of external events.

For example, the first proposition is proved by the cryptography connected with 31, 93, 418, 666, π, etc.; and the second by the concurrence of circumstance with various statements in the text such that the categories of time and causality forbid all explanations which exclude its own postulates, while the law of probabilities makes coincidence inconceivable as an evasion of the issue.

9. The Comment must be expressed in terms intelligible to the minds of men of average education, and independent of abstruse technicalities.

10. The Comment must be pertinent to the problems of our own times, and present the principles of the Law in a manner susceptible of present practical application. It must satisfy all types of intelligence, neither revolting to rational, scientific, mathematical, and philosophical thinkers, nor repugnant to religious and romantic temperaments.

11. The Comment must appeal on behalf of the Law to the authority of Experience. It must make Success the proof of the Truth of the Book of the Law at every point of contact with Reality.

The Word of Aiwaz must put forth a perfect presentation of the Universe as Necessary, Intelligible, Self-subsistent, as Integral, Absolute, and Immanent. It must satisfy all intuitions, explain all enigmas, and compose all conflicts. It must reveal Reality, reconcile Reason with Relativity; and, resolving not only all antinomies in the Absolute, but all antipathies in the appreciation of Aptness, assure the acquiescence of every faculty of mankind in the perfection of its plenary propriety.

Releasing us from every restriction upon Right, the Word of Aiwaz must extend its empire by enlisting the allegiance of every man and every woman that puts its truth to the test.

On these principles, to the pitch of my power, will I the Beast 666, who received the Book of the Law from the Mouth of mine Angel Aiwaz, make my comment thereon; being armed with the word: "But the work of the comment?

That is easy; and Hadit burning in thy heart shall make swift and secure thy pen."

Editorial Note to this Chapter.

The reader is now in full possession of the account of "how thou didst come hither". The student who wishes to act intelligently will be at pains to make himself thoroughly acquainted at the outset with the whole of the external circumstances connected with the Writing of the Book, whether they are of biographical or other importance. He should thus be able to approach the Book with his mind prepared to apprehend the unique character of their contents in respect of Its true Authorship, the peculiarities of Its methods of communicating Thought, and the nature of Its claim to be the Canon of Truth, the Key of Progress, and the Arbiter of Conduct. He will be able to form his own judgment upon It, only insofar as he is fixed in the proper Point-of-View; the sole question for him is to decide whether It is or is not that which It claims to be, the New Law in the same sense as the Vedas, the Pentateuch, the Tao Teh King, and the Qu'ran are Laws, but with the added Authority of Verbal, Literal, and Graphic inspiration established and counter-checked by internal evidence with the impeccable precision of a mathematical demonstration. If It be that, It is an unique document, valid absolutely within the terms of its self-contained thesis, incomparably more valuable than any other Transcript of Thought which we possess.

If It be not wholly that, it is a worthless curiosity of literature; worse, it is an appalling proof that no kind or degree of evidence soever is sufficient to establish any possible proposition, since the closest concatenation of circumstances may be no more than the jetsam of chance, and the most comprehensive plans of purpose a puerile pantomime. To reject this Book is to make Reason itself ridiculous and the Law of Probabilities a caprice. In Its fall it shatters the structure of Science, and buries the whole hope of man's heart in the rubble, throwing upon its heaps the sceptic, blinded, crippled, and gone melancholy mad.

The reader must face the problem squarely; half-measures will not avail. If there be aught he recognize as transcendental Truth, he cannot admit the possibility that the Speaker, taking such pains to prove Himself and His Word, should yet incorporate Falsehood in the same body, and fence it about with the same elaborate engines. If the Book be but a monument of a mortal's madness, he must tremble that such power and cunning may be the accomplices of insane and criminal arch-anarchs.

But if he know the Book to be justified of Itself, It shall be justified also of Its children; and he will glow with gladness in his heart as he reads the sixty-third to the sixty-seventh verses of Its third chapter, and gain his first glimpse of Who he himself is in truth, and to what fulfilment of Himself It is of virtue to bring Him.

CHAPTER VIII

Summary of the Case.

In this revelation is the basis of the future Aeon. Within the memory of man we have had the Pagan period, the worship of Nature, of Isis, of the Mother, of the Past; the Christian period, the worship of Man, of Osiris, of the Present. The first period is simple, quiet, easy, and pleasant; the material ignores the spiritual; the second is of suffering and death: the spiritual strives to ignore the material. Christianity and all cognate religions worship death, glorify suffering, deify corpses. The new Aeon is the worship of the spiritual made one with the material, of Horus, of the Child, of the Future.

Isis was Liberty; Osiris, bondage; but the new Liberty is that of Horus. Osiris conquered her because she did not understand him. Horus avenges both his Father and his Mother. This child Horus is a twin, two in one. Horus and Harpocrates are one, and they are also one with Set or Apophis, the destroyer of Osiris. It is by the destruction of the principle of death that they are born. The establishment of this new Aeon, this new fundamental principle, is the great work now to be accomplished in the world.

FRATER PERDURABO, to whom this revelation was made with so many signs and wonders, was himself unconvinced. He struggled against it for years. Not until the completion of His own initiation at the end of 1909 did he understand how perfectly he was bound to carry out this work.[1] Again and again He turned away from it, took it up for a few days or hours, then laid it aside. He even attempted to destroy its value, to nullify the result. Again and again the unsleeping might of the Watchers drove Him back to the work; and it was at the very moment when He thought Himself to have escaped that He found Himself fixed for ever with no possibility of again turning aside for the fraction of a second from the Path.

The history of this must one day be told by a more vivid voice. Properly considered, it is a history of continuous miracle. Enough if it is now said that in this Law lies the whole future: it is the Law of Liberty, and those who refuse it proclaim themselves slaves, and as slaves shall they be chained and flogged. It is the Law of Love, and those who refuse it declare themselves to be the children of hate, and their hate shall return upon them and consume them with its unending tortures. It is the Law of Life, and those who refuse it shall be subject to death; and death shall catch them unawares. Even their life shall be a living death. It is the Law of Light, and those who refuse it thereby make themselves dark for ever.

Do what thou wilt shall be the whole of the Law! Refuse this, and fall under the curse of destiny. Divide will against itself, the result is impotence and strife, strife-in-vain. The Law condemns no man. Accept the Law, and everything is

[1] Indeed, it was not until his Word became conterminous with Himself and His Universe that all alien ideas lost their meaning for Him.

lawful. Refuse the Law, you put yourself beyond its pale. It is the Law that Jesus Christ, or rather the Gnostic tradition of which the Christ-legend is a degradation, attempted to teach; but nearly every word he[1] said was misinterpreted and garbled by his enemies, particularly by those who called themselves his disciples. In any case the Aeon was not ready for a Law of Freedom. Of all his followers only St. Augustine appears to have got even a glimmer of what he meant.

A further attempt to teach this law was made through Sir Edward Kelly at the end of the sixteenth century. The bondage of orthodoxy prevented his words from being heard, or understood. In many other ways has the spirit of truth striven with man, and partial shadows of this truth have been the greatest allies of science and philosophy. Only now has success been attained. A perfect vehicle was found, and the message enshrined in a jewelled casket; that is to say, in a book with the injunction "Change not as much as the style of a letter." This book is reproduced in facsimile, in order that there shall be no possibility of corrupting it. Here, then, we have an absolutely fixed and definite standpoint for the foundation of an universal religion.

We have the Key to the resolution of all human problems, both philosophical and practical. If we have seemed to labour

[1] Consult Equinox III 2 "Jesus," a study of the New Testament by The Beast 666, where it is proven that "Jesus" is a composite figure of several incompatible elements. There is therefore no "he" in the case. The Gospels are a crude compilation of Gnosticism, Judaism, Essenism, Hinduism, Buddhism, with the watch-words of various sacerdotal-political cults, thrown at random into a hotch-potch of the distorted legends of the persons of the Pagan Pantheon, all glued with a semblance of unity in the interests of sustaining the shaken fabric of local faiths against the assaults of the consolidation of civilization, and of applying the cooperative principle to businesses whose throats were being cut by competition.

at proof, our love must be the excuse for our infirmity ; for we know well that which is written in the Book :

" Success is your proof."

We ask no more than one witness ; and we call upon Time to take the Oath, and testify to the Truth of our plea.

אלהים ☉ 3·141593 = π to 6 places
האד = HAD = 11 = in full = 555 = 5 ENERGY
לא = 31. אל = 31.
☉ = σ (= 6) = XX + XI = 31.
שט = 309 = XX + XI.
Η ΚΟΚΚΙΝΗ ΓΥΝΗ = 667 = Η·Κ·Γ = 31.
נו = NU = 56.
161 COPH NIA כף = 100 + אין = 61
כף = כ in full = ☉ + ☽ in Greek. see I 46-47.
AIWASS AIVAS = 78. (666's Error)
TA-Nish TANICh = 78. Alternatively
Sh for Ch gives 370. O Sh, Creation
עיוז AIWAZ = 93.
ΘΕΛΗΜΑ = 93 in full 2542. } see I
ΛΟΓΟC ΠΥΘΙΟC ΤΟΥ ΝΟΜΟΥ } sq.
ΑΓΑΠΗ = 93.
M····M = 93.
III° + + + + = 93.
עבא = 93 WILL: also Star, Host.
Montu MVNTV = 111
RPST = 311.
חאבש = KHABS = 311 = BHTA.
AIFACC: AIWASS = 418.
RPSTOVAL בולשכין = 418.
ABRAHADABRA = 418.
Ch = 8 = ChITh = 418 = ABRAHADABRA
= RA + HVVR (RA-HOOR).
ΠΑΛΛΑC ΑΘΗΝΗ = 418.
ΤΟ ΜΗ = 418.
PARZIVAL = 418.
חית (ח = 8 in full) = 418.
St Betsayfa בהטישאיפא = 418.

HRV-RA-HA = 211 + 201 + 6 = 418.
הרו = HERU = 211 }
רא = RA = 201 } 418.
הא = HA = 26 }
הוור = HOOR = 217 } 418 }
רא = RA = 201 } } 444.
כו = KHU = 26 }
ΝΟΜΟC = 430
ΜΟΥ = 510 = ΦΙ = ריש
תריון = THERION = 666.
ΤΟ ΜΕΓΑ ΘΗΡΙΟΝ = 666.
KAMURET = 666
666 The number of the STELE
the number of The BEAST. The
NUMBER of THE MAN see Apocalypse
The Beast AChIHA 666 in full.
(The usual spelling is ChIVA)
A = 111. Ch = 418. I = 20. H = 6. A = 111.
O = A in THE Book of THOTH (The TAROT).
A = 111 ☉ = 6
ANKH-F-N-KHONShU-T = 666.
Nuteru NVThIRV = 666.
CΤΗΛΗ 666 = 52 + 666 = 718
Bes-n-maut BISh NA-MAVT } = 888
TA-Nich Th A-NICh } = Ch × A
ΛΟΓΟS ΠΥΘΙΟC = WORD = 1142.
ΑΓΕ ΤΟ ΘΕΛΗΜΑ CΟΥ = 1142.

A FEW INDICATIONS FOR THE
STUDENT OF THE LINE TO BE
ADOPTED IN HIS ELUCIDATION OF

LIBER · AL

A L

(LIBER LEGIS)

THE BOOK OF THE LAW

sub figura xxxi

as delivered by

93 —AIWASS— 418

to

Ankh-f-n-khonsu

The Priest of the Princes
who is

6 6 6

A.∴A.∴
Publication in Class A.

Had! The manifestation of Nuit
The unveiling of the company of heaven
Every man and every woman is a star
Every number is infinite: there is no difference
Help me, o warrior lord of Thebes, in my
unveiling before the Children of men
Be thou Hadit, my secret centre, my
heart & my tongue.
Behold! it is revealed by Aiwass the
minister of Hoor-paar-kraat
The Khabs is in the Khu, not the Khu in
the Khabs
Worship then the Khabs, and behold my
light shed over you.

Let my servants be few & secret: they shall
rule the many & the known.
These are fools that men adore; both their
Gods & their men are fools.
Come forth, o children, under the stars
& take your fill of love. I am above you
and in you. My ecstasy is in yours My
joy is to see your joy

V.1. of Spell called the Joy.

Now ye shall know that the chosen
priest & apostle of infinite space is
the prince-priest the Beast and in

his woman; called the Scarlet Woman, is
all power given. They shall gather my
children into their fold: they shall bring the
glory of the stars into the hearts of men.
For he is ever a sun, and she a moon. But
to him is the winged secret flame and to
her the stooping starlight.
But ye are not so chosen
Burn upon their brows, o splendrous serpent!
O azure-lidded woman, bend upon them!
The key of the rituals is in the secret word
which I have given unto him

With the God & the Adorer I am nothing: they do not see me. They are as upon the earth I am Heaven, and there is no other God than me, and my lord Hadit.

Now therefore I am known to ye by my name Nuit, and to him by a secret name which I will give him when at last he knoweth me

Since I am Infinite Space and the Infinite Stars thereof do ye also thus. Bind nothing! Let there be no difference made among you between any one thing & any other thing; for thereby there cometh hurt.

But whoso availeth in this, let him be the chief of all!

I am Nuit and my word is six and fifty

Divide, add, multiply and understand.

Then saith the prophet and slave of the beauteous one. Who am I, and what shall be the sign. So she answered him, bending down, a lambent flame of blue, all-touching all penetrant, her lovely hands upon the black earth & her lithe body arched for love and her soft feet not hurting the little flowers Thou knowest! And the sign shall be my ecstasy, the consciousness of the continuity of existence, the ~~non-atomic~~ ~~the unfragmentary~~ ~~non-atomic fact of my universality~~. the omnipresence of my body.

(~~Write this in whiter words~~) | Done later as above.

(~~But go forth on~~)

Then the priest answered & said unto the Queen of Space, kissing her lovely brows and the dew of her light bathing his whole body in a sweet-smelling perfume of sweat O Nuit, continuous one of Heaven, let it be ever thus that men speak not of thee as One but as None and let them speak not of thee at all since thou art continuous.

None, cleaved the light, faint of faery, of the stars, and two. For I am divided for love's sake, for the chance of union.

This is the creation of the world that the pain of ~~distance~~ division is as nothing and the joy of dissolution all.

For these fools of men and their

woes care not thou at all! They feel
little; what is, is balanced by weak
joys: but ye are my chosen ones.

Obey my prophet! follow out the
ordeals of my knowledge! seek me
only! Then the joys of my love will
redeem ye from all pain. This is
so: I swear it by the vault of my
body; by my sacred heart and tongue;
by all I can give, by all I desire of
ye all.
Then the priest fell into a deep trance or

swoon & said unto the Queen of Heaven
Write unto us the ordeals write unto
us the rituals write unto us the law.
But she said the ordeals I write not
the rituals shall be half known and
half concealed: the Law is for all
This that thou writest is the threefold
book of Law
My scribe Ankh-af-na-khonsu the
priest of the princes shall not in one
letter change this book; but lest there
be folly, he shall comment thereupon
by the wisdom of Ra-Hoor-Khuit.

Also the mantras and spells; the
obeah and the wanga; the work of
the wand and the work of the
Sword: these he shall learn and teach.
He must teach; but he may make severe
the ordeals.

The word of the Law is Θελημα.
Who calls us Thelemites will do no
wrong, if he look but close into the
word. For there are therein Three
Grades. the Hermit and the Lover and
the man of Earth. Do what thou wilt

shall be the whole of the Law.
The word of Sin is Restriction. O man!
refuse not thy wife if she will. O
lover, if thou wilt, depart. There is
no bond that can unite the divided but
love: all else is a curse. Accursèd!
Accursèd! be it to the aeons. Hell.
Let it be that state of manyhood
bound and loathing. So with thy all
thou hast no right but to do thy will
Do that and no other shall say nay.
For pure will, unassuaged of purpose,

delivered from the lust of result, is
every way perfect.
The Perfect and the Perfect are one
Perfect and not two; nay, are none!
Nothing is a secret key of this law.
Sixty-one the Jews call it; I call it
Eight, eighty, four hundred & eighteen.
But they have the half: unite by thine
art so that all disappear.
My prophet is a fool with his one one
one; are not they the Ox and none
by the Book.

Abrogate are all rituals, all ordeals, all
words and signs. Ra-Hoor-Khuit hath
taken his seat in the East at the Equinox
of the Gods and let Asar be with Isa
who also are one. But they are not of
me. Let Asar be the adorant, Isa the
sufferer; Hoor in his secret name and
splendour is the Lord initiating.
There is a word to say about the Hierophantic
task. Behold! there are three ordeals in
one, and it may be given in three ways.
The gross must pass through fire; let the

fine be tried in intellect, and the lofty ones in the highest. Thus ye have star & star, system & system; let not one know well the other.

There are four gates to one palace; the floor of that palace is of silver and gold, lapis lazuli & jasper are there, and all rare scents jasmine & rose, and the emblems of death. Let him enter in turn or at once the four gates; let him stand on the floor of the palace. Will he not sink? Amn. Ho! warrior, if thy servant sink? But there are means and means. Be goodly therefore: dress ye all in fine apparel eat rich foods and drink sweet wines and wines that foam. ~~but~~ Also, take your fill and will of love as ye will, when, where and with whom ye will. But always unto me. If this be not aright; if ye confound the space-marks, saying: They are one or saying They are many; if the ritual be not ever unto me: then expect the direful judgments of Ra Hoor Khuit. This shall regenerate the world, the little

world my sister, my heart & my tongue,
unto whom I send this kiss. Also, o
scribe and prophet though thou be of the
princes it shall not assuage thee nor
absolve thee. But ecstasy be thine and
joy of earth: ever To me To me
Change not as much as the style
of a letter; for behold thou o prophet
shalt not behold all these mysteries
hidden therein.
The child of thy bowels, he shall behold
them.
Expect him not from the East nor from

the West, for from no expected house cometh that child. Aum! All words are sacred and all prophets true; save only that they understand a little; solve the first half of the equation, leave the second unattacked. But thou hast all in the clear light, and some though not all in the dark.

Invoke me under my stars. Love is the law, love under will. Nor let the fools mistake love; for there are love and love. There is the dove and there is the serpent. Choose ye well! He, my prophet, hath chosen, knowing the law of the fortress and the great mystery of the House of God.

All these old letters of my Book are aright; but צ is not the Star. This also is secret: my prophet shall reveal it to the wise.

I give unimaginable joys on earth: certainty, not faith, while in life, upon death; peace unutterable, rest, ecstasy: nor do I demand aught in sacrifice.

My incense is of resinous woods & gums and there is no blood therein: because of my hair the trees of Eternity.

My number is 11, as all their numbers who are of us. (Lost) [illegible] The shape of my star is The Five Pointed Star, with a Circle in the Middle, & the circle is Red. My colour is black to the blind, but the blue & gold are seen of the seeing. Also I have a secret glory for them that love me.

But to love me is better than all things: if under the night-stars in the desert thou presently burnest mine incense before me invoking me with a pure heart and the Serpent flame therein, thou shalt come a little to lie in my bosom. For one kiss wilt thou then be willing to give all:

but whoso gives one particle of dust
shall lose all in that hour. Ye shall
gather goods and store of women and
spices; ye shall wear rich jewels; ye
shall exceed the nations of the earth
in splendour & pride; but always in the
love of me, and so shall ye come to
my joy. I charge you earnestly to come
before me in a single robe and covered
with a rich headdress. I love you I yearn to
you. Pale or purple, veiled or voluptuous, I
who am all pleasure and purple

and drunkenness of the innermost sense
desire you. Put on the wings and arouse
the coiled splendour within you: come unto me
At all my meetings with you shall the
priestess say – and her eyes shall burn
with desire as she stands bare and rejoicing
in my secret temple – To me! To me!
calling forth the flame of the hearts of all in her
love-chant.
Sing the rapturous love-song unto me!
Burn to me perfumes! Wear to me jewels!
Drink to me, for I love you! I love you!

I am the blue-lidded daughter of Sunset; I am the naked brilliance of the voluptuous night-sky.

To me! To me!

The Manifestation of Nuit is at an end.

End.

1 Nu! the hiding of Hadit.

2 Come! all ye, and learn the secret that
hath not yet been revealed. I Hadit am
the complement of Nu my bride. I am not
extended, and Khabs is the name of my House.

3 In the sphere I am everywhere, the centre, as
she, the circumference, is nowhere found.

4 Yet she shall be known & I never.

5 Behold! the rituals of the old time are black.
Let the evil ones be cast away; let the
good ones be purged by the prophet! Then shall
this Knowledge go aright.

6. I am the flame that burns in every heart of
man, and in the core of every star. I am

Life, and the giver of Life; yet therefore is the knowledge of me the knowledge of death.

7. I am the Magician and the Exorcist. I am the axle of the wheel, and the cube in the circle. "Come unto me" is a foolish word; for it is I that go.

8 Who worshipped Heru-pa-kraath have worshipped me; ill, for I am the worshipper.

9 Remember all ye that existence is pure joy; that all the sorrows are but as shadows; they pass & are done; but there is that which remains.

10. O prophet! thou hast ill will to learn this writing.

11. I see thee hate the hand & the pen; but I am

12 Because of me in Thee which thou knewest not

13. for why? Because thou wast the knower,
and me.

14. Now let there be a veiling of this shrine: now
let the light devour men and eat them
up with blindness.

15. For I am perfect, being Not; and my number
is nine by the fools; but with the just I am
Eight, and one in Eight: Which is vital, for
I am none indeed. The Empress and the King
are not of me; for there is a further secret.

16 I am The Empress & the Hierophant. Thus
eleven as my bride is eleven.

17 Hear me, ye people of sighing!
The sorrows of pain and regret
Are left to the dead and the dying,
The folk that not know me as yet.
18 These are dead, these fellows; they feel not. We
are not for the poor and sad: the lords of the
earth are our kinsfolk.
19 Is a God to live in a dog? No! but the
highest are of us. They shall rejoice, our chosen:
who sorroweth is not of us.
20 Beauty and strength, leaping laughter and
delicious languor, force and fire, are of us.

21 We have nothing with the outcast and the unfit:
let them die in their misery: For they feel
not. Compassion is the vice of kings: stamp
down the wretched & the weak: this is the
law of the strong: this is our law and the
joy of the world. Think not, o king, upon that
lie: That Thou Must Die: verily thou shalt
not die, but live! Now let it be understood
If the body of the King dissolve, he shall remain
in pure ecstasy for ever Nuit Hadit Ra-Hoor
Khuit. The Sun, Strength & Sight, Light these
are for the servants of the Star & the Snake

22 I am the Snake that giveth Knowledge & Delight
and bright glory, and stir the hearts of men
with drunkenness. To worship me take wine
and strange drugs whereof I will tell my
prophet, & be drunk thereof! They shall not
harm ye at all. It is a lie, this folly
against self. The exposure of innocence
is a lie. Be strong, o man, lust, enjoy
all things of sense and rapture: fear not
that any God shall deny thee for this.
23 I am alone: there is no God where I am.
24 Behold! these be grave mysteries; for there
are also of my friends who be hermits. Now

think not to find them in the forest or on the
mountain; but in beds of purple, caressed by
magnificent beasts of women with large limbs,
and fire and light in their eyes, and masses
of flaming hair about them; there shall ye
find them. Ye shall see them at rule, at
victorious armies, at all the joy; and there
shall be in them a joy a million times
greater than this. Beware lest any
force another, King against King! Love one
another with burning hearts; on the low men
trample in the fierce lust of your pride

in the day of your wrath.

25. Ye are against the people, O my chosen!

26. I am the secret Serpent coiled about to spring: in my coiling there is joy. If I lift up my head, I and my Nuit are one. If I droop down mine head, and shoot forth venom, then is rapture of the earth, and I and the earth are one.

27. There is great danger in me; for who doth not understand these runes shall make a great miss. He shall fall down into the pit called Because, and there he shall

perish with the dogs of Reason.

28 Now a curse upon Because and his kin!

29 May Because be accursèd for ever!

30 If Will stops and cries Why, invoking Because, then Will stops & does nought.

31 If Power asks why, then is Power weakness.

32 Also reason is a lie; for there is a factor infinite & unknown; & all their words are skew-wise.

33 Enough of Because! Be he damned for a dog!

34. But ye, o my people, rise up & awake!

35. Let the rituals be rightly performed with joy & beauty!

36 There are rituals of the elements and feasts of the times.

37 A feast for the first night of the Prophet and his Bride!

38 A feast for the three days of the writing of the Book of the Law.

39 A feast for Tahuti and the child of the Prophet—secret, O Prophet!

40 A feast for the Supreme Ritual, and a feast for the Equinox of the Gods.

41 A feast for fire and a feast for water; a feast for life and a greater feast for death

42 A feast every day in your hearts in the joy of my rapture.

43 A feast every night unto Nu, and the pleasure of uttermost delight.

44 Aye! feast! rejoice! there is no dread hereafter. There is the dissolution, and eternal ecstasy in the kisses of Nu.

45 There is death for the dogs.

46 Dost thou fail? Art thou sorry? Is fear in thine heart?

47 Where I am these are not.

48 Pity not the fallen! I never knew them.
I am not for them. I console not: I hate
the consoled & the consoler.

49 I am unique & conqueror. I am not of the
slaves that perish. Be they damned &
dead! Amen. [This is of the 4: there is
a fifth who is invisible & therein am I
as a babe in an egg.]

50 Blue am I and gold in the light of my
bride: but the red gleam is in my eyes
& my spangles are purple & green.

51. Purple beyond purple: it is the light higher

than eyesight.
52 There is a veil: that veil is black. It is
the veil of the modest woman; it is the veil
of sorrow, & the pall of death: this is none
of me. Tear down that lying spectre of
the centuries: veil not your vices in
virtuous words: these vices are my service;
ye do well, & I will reward you here and
hereafter.
53 Fear not, o prophet, when these words are
said, thou shalt not be sorry. Thou art
emphatically my chosen; and blessed are

the eyes that thou shalt look upon with
gladness. But I will hide thee in a
mask of sorrow: they that see thee shall
fear thou art fallen: but I lift thee up.
54 Nor shall they who cry aloud their folly
that thou meanest nought avail; thou
shall reveal it: thou availest: they are
the slaves of because: They are not of
me. The stops as thou wilt; the letters
change them not in style or value!
55 Thou shalt obtain the order & value of
the English Alphabet; thou shalt find

new symbols to attribute them unto.

56 Begone! ye mockers; even though ye laugh
in my honour ye shall laugh not long: then
when ye are sad know that I have
forsaken you.

57. He that is righteous shall be righteous still;
he that is filthy shall be filthy still.

58 Yea! deem not of change: ye shall be as ye
are, & not other. Therefore the kings of
the earth shall be Kings for ever: the slaves
shall serve. There is none that shall
be cast down or lifted up: all is ever

as it was. Yet there are masked ones my servants: it may be that yonder beggar is a King. A King may choose his garment as he will: there is no certain test: but a beggar cannot hide his poverty.

59 Beware therefore! Love all, lest perchance is a King concealed! Say you so? Fool! If he be a King, thou canst not hurt him.

60 Therefore strike hard & low and to hell with them, master!

61 There is a light before thine eyes o prophet a light undesired, most desirable.

62 I am uplifted in thine heart and the kisses
of the stars rain hard upon thy body.
63 Thou art exhaust in the voluptuous fullness
of the aspiration: the aspiration is sweeter
than death, more rapid and laughterful than
a caress of Hell's own worm.
64 Oh! thou art overcome: we are upon thee;
our delight is all over thee: hail! hail!
prophet of Nu! prophet of Had! prophet of
Ra-Hoor-Khu! Now rejoice! now come in
our splendour & rapture! Come in our passionate
peace, & write sweet words for the Kings!

65 I am the Master: thou art the Holy Chosen One.
66 Write, & find ecstasy in writing! Work &
be our bed in working! Thrill with the
Joy of life & death! Ah! thy death shall
be lovely: whoso seeth it shall be glad. Thy
death shall be the seal of the promise of
our agelong love. Come! lift up thine heart
& rejoice! We are one; we are none.
67 Hold! Hold! Bear up in thy rapture;
fall not in swoon of the excellent kisses!
68 Harden! Hold up thyself! Lift thine head!

breathe not so deep — die!

69 Ah! Ah! What do I feel? Is the word
Exhausted?

70 There is help & hope in other spells. Wisdom
says: be strong! Then canst thou bear more
joy. Be not animal; refine thy rapture!
If thou drink, drink by the eight and ninety
rules of art: if thou love, exceed by
delicacy; and if thou do aught joyous, let
there be subtlety therein!

71 But exceed! exceed!

72 Strive ever to more! and if thou art truly

mine – and doubt it if not, an if thou art
ever joyous! – death is the crown of all
73 Ah Ah! Death! Death! thou shalt long for
death. Death is forbidden, O man, unto thee.
74 The length of thy longing shall be the strength
of its glory. He that lives long & desires
death much is ever the King among the Kings.
75 Aye! listen to the numbers & the words:
76 4 6 3 8 A B K 2 4 A L G M O R 3 Y
X 24 89 R P S T O V A L. What
meaneth this, O prophet? Thou knowest
not, nor shalt thou know ever. There
cometh one to follow thee: he shall

Expound it. But remember, o chosen
one, to be me; to follow the love of
Nu in the star-lit heaven; to look forth
upon men, to tell them this glad word.
77 O be thou proud and mighty among men!
78 Lift up thyself! for there is none like unto
thee among men or among Gods! Lift up
thyself, o my prophet, thy stature shall
surpass the stars. They shall worship thy
name, foursquare, mystic, wonderful, the
number of the man; and the name of

Thy house 418.

79 The end of the hiding of Hadit; and
blessing & worship to the prophet of
the lovely Star.

1 Abrahadabra! the reward of Ra Hoor Khut.
2 There is division hither homeward; there is a
word not known. Spelling is defunct; all is not
aught. Beware! Hold! Raise the spell of
Ra-Hoor-Khuit.
3 Now let it be first understood that I am
a god of War and of Vengeance. I shall
deal hardly with them.
4 Choose ye an island!
5 Fortify it!
6 Dung it about with enginery of war!
7 I will give you a war-engine.
8 With it ye shall smite the peoples and

none shall stand before you.
9 Lurk! Withdraw! Upon them! this
is the Law of the Battle of Conquest: thus
shall my worship be about my secret house
10 Get the stélé of revealing itself; set it
in thy secret temple — and that temple
is already aright disposed — & it shall be your
Kiblah for ever. It shall not fade, but
miraculous colour shall come back to it
day after day. Close it in locked glass for a
proof to the world.
11 This shall be your only proof. I forbid argument.
Conquer! That is enough. I will make easy

to you the abstruction from the ill-ordered house in the Victorious City. Thou shalt thyself convey it with worship, o prophet, though thou likest it not. Thou shalt have danger & trouble. Ra-Hoor-Khu is with thee. Worship me with fire & blood; worship me with swords & with spears. Let the woman be girt with a sword before me: let blood flow to my name. Trample down the Heathen; be upon them, o warrior, I will give you of their flesh to eat!

12 Sacrifice cattle little and big: after a child.

13 But not now.

14 Ye shall see that hour, o blessed Beast, and
thou the Scarlet Concubine of his desire!

15 Ye shall be sad thereof.

16 Seem not too eagerly to catch the promises; fear
not to undergo the curses. Ye, even ye, know not
this meaning all.

17 Fear not at all; fear neither men, nor Fates,
nor gods, nor anything. Money fear not, nor
laughter of the folk folly, nor any other power
in heaven or upon the earth or under the
earth. Nu is your refuge as Hadit your

light; and I am the strength, force, vigour, of
your arms.
18 Mercy let be off: damn them who pity.
Kill and torture; spare not; be upon them.
19 That stélé they shall call the Abomination
of Desolation; count well its name, & it shall
be to you as 718.
20 Why? Because of the fall of Because, that
he is not there again.
21 Set up my image in the East: thou shalt buy
thee an image which I will show thee, especial,
not unlike the one thou knowest. And it shall
be suddenly easy for thee to do this.

22. The other images group around me to support
me: let all be worshipped, for they shall
cluster to exalt me. I am the visible object
of worship; the others are secret; for the Beast
& his Bride are they: and for the winners of
the Ordeal x. What is this? Thou shalt know.
23 For perfume mix meal & honey & thick leavings
of red wine: then oil of Abramelin and
olive oil, and afterward soften & smooth
down with rich fresh blood!
24 The best blood is of the moon, monthly: then
the fresh blood of a child, or dropping from the

host of heaven: then of enemies; then
of the priest or of the worshippers: last of
some beast, no matter what.

25 This burn: of this make cakes & eat unto
me. This hath also another use; let it be
laid before me, and kept thick with perfumes
of your orison: it shall become full of beetles
as it were and creeping things sacred unto me.

26 These slay, naming your enemies & they shall
fall before you.

27 Also these shall breed lust & power of lust in
you at the eating thereof.

28 Also ye shall be strong in war.

29 Moreover, be they long kept, it is better; for
they swell with my force. All before me.
30 My altar is of open brass work: burn thereon
in silver or gold.
31 There cometh a rich man from the West who
shall pour his gold upon thee.
32 From gold forge steel:
33 Be ready to fly or to smite.
34 But your holy place shall be untouched
throughout the centuries: though with fire and
sword it be burnt down & shattered, yet
an invisible house there standeth and
shall stand until the fall of the Great

Equinox, when Hrumachis shall arise and the double-wanded one assume my throne and place. Another prophet shall arise, and bring fresh fever from the skies; another woman shall wake the lust & worship of the Snake; another soul of God and beast shall mingle in the globèd priest; another sacrifice shall stain the tomb; another king shall reign; and. blessing no longer be poured To the Hawk-headed mystical Lord!

35 The half of the word of Heru-ra-ha, called Hoor-pa-kraat and Ra-Hoor-Khut.

36 Then said the prophet unto the God.

37 I adore thee in the song
"I am the Lord of Thebes" &c from vellum book
unity &c
——— "fill me"

38 So that thy light is in me & its red flame
is as a sword in my hand to push thy
order. There is a secret door that I shall
make to establish thy way in all the quarters
(these are the adorations, as thou hast written)
as it is said

"The light is mine" &c
from vellum book to "Ra-Hoor-Khuit"

39 All this and a book to say how thou
didst come hither and a reproduction of
this ink and paper for ever — for in it is
the word secret & not only in the English —
and thy comment upon this the Book of the Law
shall be printed beautifully in red ink and
black upon beautiful paper made by hand;
and to each man and woman that thou
meetest, were it but to dine or to drink
at them, it is the Law to give. Then they
shall chance to abide in this bliss or no;
it is no odds. Do this quickly!

40 But the work of the comment? That is easy; and

Hadit burning in thy heart shall make swift and secure thy pen.

41. Establish at thy Kaaba a clerk-house: all must be done well and with business way.

42. The ordeals thou shalt oversee thyself, save only the blind ones. Refuse none, but thou shalt know & destroy the traitors. I am Ra-Hoor-Khuit and I am powerful to protect my servant. Success is thy proof: argue not; convert not: talk not overmuch. Them that seek to entrap thee, to overthrow thee, them attack without pity or quarter & destroy them utterly. Swift as a trodden serpent turn..

and strike! Be thou yet deadlier than he!
42 Drag down their souls to awful torment: laugh
at their fear: spit upon them!
43 Let the Scarlet Woman beware! If pity and
compassion and tenderness visit her heart
if she leave my work to toy with old
sweetnesses then shall my vengeance be
known. I will slay me her child: I will
alienate her heart: I will cast her out
from men: as a shrinking and despised harlot
shall she crawl through dusk wet streets, and
die cold and an-hungered.

44. But let her raise herself in pride. Let
her follow me in my way. Let her
work the work of wickedness! Let her kill
her heart! Let her be loud and adulterous;
let her be covered with jewels and rich
garments, and let her be shameless before
all men!

45 Then will I lift her to pinnacles of power:
then will I breed from her a child mightier
than all the kings of the earth. I will fill
her with joy: with my force shall she see
& strike at the worship of Nu. she shall
achieve Hadit.

46. I am the warrior Lord of the Forties: the
Eighties cower before me, & are abased
I will bring you to victory & joy: I will be
at your arms in battle & ye shall
delight to slay. Success is your proof;
courage is your armour; go on, go on, in
my strength & ye shall turn not back for
any.
47 This book shall be translated into all
tongues: but always with the original in
the writing of the Beast; for in the

chance shape of the letters and their
position to one another: in these are mysteries
that no Beast shall divine. Let him
not seek to try: but one cometh after
him, whence I say not, who shall
discover the Key of it all. Then
this line drawn is a key: then this
circle squared ⊕ in its failure is a
key also. And Abrahadabra. It shall
be his child & that strangely. Let him not
seek after this; for thereby alone can he
fall from it.

48 Now this mystery of the letters is done, and
I want to go on to the holier place.
49 I am in a secret fourfold word the blasphemy against
all gods of men.
50 Curse them! Curse them! Curse them!
51 With my Hawk's head I peck at the eyes of
Jesus as he hangs upon the cross
52 I flap my wings in the face of Mohammed &
blind him
53 With my claws I tear out the flesh of the
Indian and the Buddhist, Mongol and
Din.
54 Bahlasti! Ompehda! I spit on your

crapulous creeds.

55 Let Mary inviolate be torn upon wheels: for her sake let all chaste women be utterly despised among you.

56 Also for beauty's sake and love's.

57 Despise also all cowards; professional soldiers who dare not fight, but play: all fools despise!

58 But the keen and the proud, the royal and the lofty; ye are brothers!

59 As brothers fight ye.

60 There is no law beyond Do what thou wilt.

61 There is an end of the word of the God

enthroned in Ra's seat, lightening the girdles
of the soul.

62 To Me do ye reverence; to me come ye
through tribulation of ordeal, which is
bliss.

63 The fool readeth this Book of the Law, and
its comment & he understandeth it not.

64 Let him come through the first ordeal &
it will be to him as silver

65 Through the second gold

66 Through the third, stones of precious water.

67 Through the fourth, ultimate sparks of the
intimate fire.

68 Yet to all it shall seem beautiful. Its
enemies who say not so, are mere liars.
69 There is success
70 I am the Hawk-Headed Lord of Silence
& of Strength; my nemyss shrouds the
night-blue sky.
71 Hail! ye twin warriors about the pillars of
the world! for your time is nigh at hand
72 I am the Lord of the Double Wand of Power
the wand of the ~~[illegible]~~ Force of Coph Nia — I but my
left hand is empty, for I have crushed

an Universe & nought remains.

73 Paste the sheets from right to left and from top to bottom: then behold!

74 There is a splendour in my name hidden and glorious, as the sun of midnight is ever the son

75 The ending of the words is the Word Abrahadabra.

The Book of the Law is Written and Concealed

Aum. Ha.

THE COMMENT

Do what thou wilt shall be the whole of the Law.

The study of this Book is forbidden. It is wise to destroy this copy after the first reading.

Whosoever disregards this does so at his own risk and peril. These are most dire.

Those who discuss the contents of this Book are to be shunned by all, as centres of pestilence.

All questions of the Law are to be decided only by appeal to my writings, each for himself.

There is no law beyond Do what thou wilt.

Love is the law, love under will.

The priest of the princes,

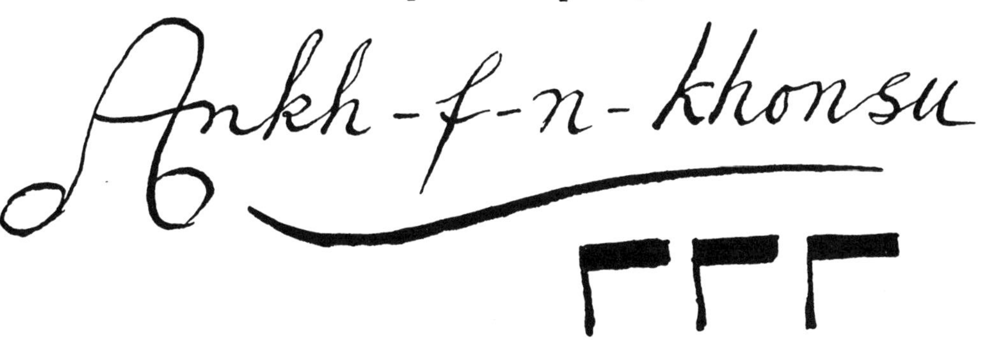